WELCOME TO
HOW IT WORKS
Annual

Welcome to the ninth volume of the How It Works Annual, where your burning questions about how the world ticks finally get answered. Feed your mind, indulge your curiosity and uncover the truth behind some of the most popular misconceptions. We delve deep into the mysteries of our world with in-depth and entertaining articles, accompanied by cutaways, illustrations and incredible images to show you exactly what goes on inside. The How It Works Annual explores the universe through six areas of knowledge: technology, transport, the environment, history, science and space. Our subjects range from super volcanoes and prehistoric wildlife, to the future of technology and the greatest engineering feats of the modern world. In this edition, you'll also find a myth-busting special where we explore some of the most common misconceptions and unravel some of the strangest conspiracy theories. We've also got features on incredible space weather, supersonic stealth jets, experiments that changed the world and whether humans are still evolving.
Are you ready to learn more about the world around you?
Then read on and be amazed.

HOW IT WORKS
Annual

Future PLC Richmond House, 33 Richmond Hill,
Bournemouth, Dorset, BH2 6EZ

Editorial
Editor **Dan Peel**
Senior Art Editor **Duncan Crook**
Editorial Director **Jon White**
Senior Art Editor **Andy Downes**

Cover images
Getty, Alamy, Science Photo Library

Photography
All copyrights and trademarks are recognised and respected

Advertising
Media packs are available on request
Commercial Director **Clare Dove**
clare.dove@futurenet.com

International
International Licensing Director **Matt Ellis**
matt.ellis@futurenet.com

Circulation
Head of Newstrade **Tim Mathers**

Production
Head of Production **Mark Constance**
Production Project Manager **Clare Scott**
Advertising Production Manager **Joanne Crosby**
Digital Editions Controller **Jason Hudson**
Production Managers **Keely Miller, Nola Cokely,
Vivienne Calvert, Fran Twentyman**

Management
Chief Operations Officer **Aaron Asadi**
Commercial Finance Director **Dan Jotcham**
Head of Art & Design **Greg Whitaker**

Printed by William Gibbons, 26 Planetary Road,
Willenhall, West Midlands, WV13 3XT

Distributed by Marketforce, 5 Churchill Place, Canary Wharf, London, E14 5HU
www.marketforce.co.uk Tel: 0203 787 9001

How It Works Annual Volume 9
© 2018 Future Publishing Limited

FUTURE
Connectors.
Creators.
Experience
Makers.

Future plc is a public
company quoted on the
London Stock Exchange
(symbol: FUTR)
www.futureplc.com

Chief executive **Zillah Byng-Thorne**
Chairman **Richard Huntingford**
Chief financial officer **Penny Ladkin-Brand**

Tel +44 (0)1225 442 244

C★NTENTS

018

040

026

052

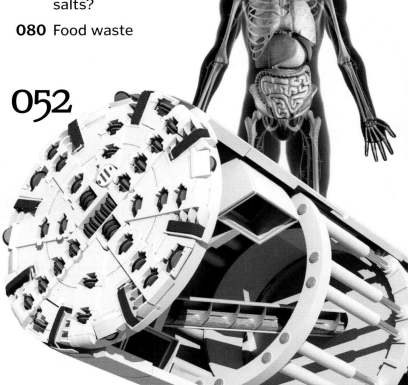

062

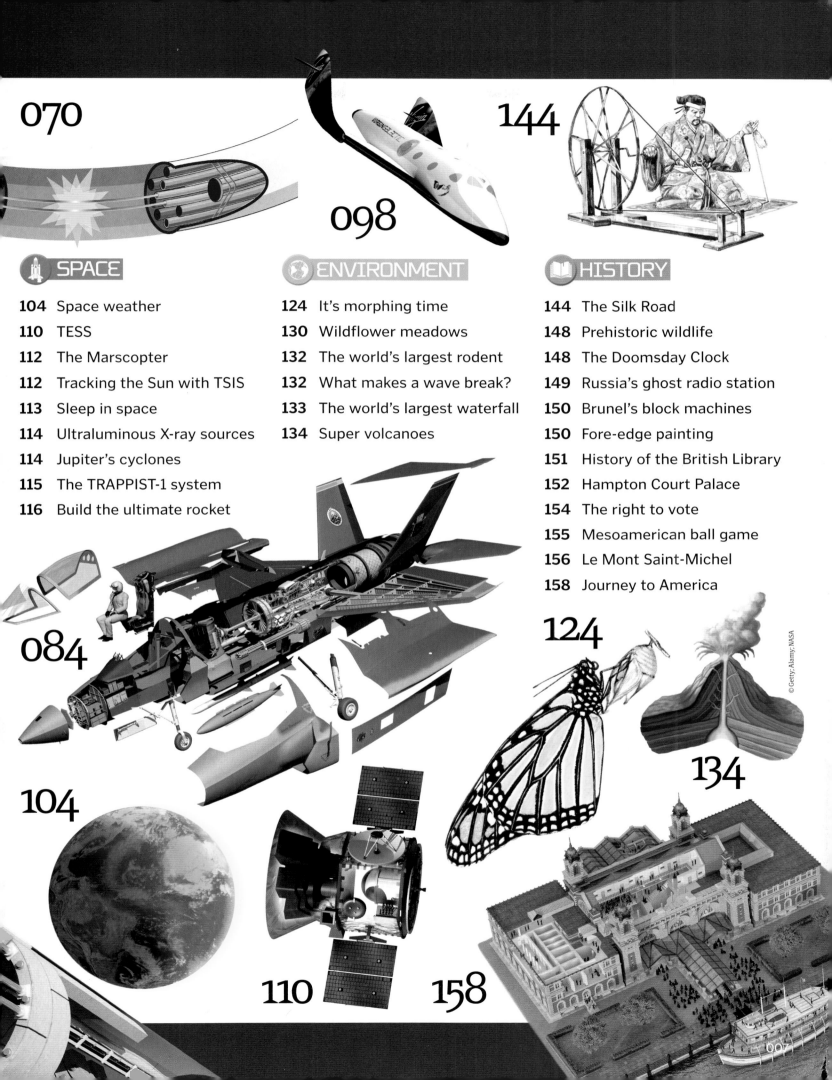

070

098

144

084

104

110

124

134

158

© Getty; Alamy; NASA

DOES IT TAKE 7 YEARS TO DIGEST GUM?

CAN YOUR PHONE BRING A PLANE DOWN?

DO WE ONLY USE **10%** OF OUR
BRAIN POWER?

REVEALED THE TRUTH BEHIND OVER **50** MYTHS, MISCONCEPTIONS & CONSPIRACIES

DID HUMANS EVOLVE FROM CHIMPS?

WOULD YOU EXPLODE WITHOUT A SPACESUIT?

Discover the truth behind the myths and the psychology of the believers

"THE MOON LANDINGS WERE FAKED"

Nearly 50 years on from what is possibly humanity's greatest achievement, conspiracy theorists have pored over the footage of the Moon landings from 1969 and they think it's a set up. They believe NASA built a studio on Earth, attached actors to wires and simulated low gravity with slow-motion filming, all to trump their Soviet rivals in the space race. NASA says they put men on the Moon. So, what really happened?

The lighting has been a topic of much debate, with conspiracy theorists claiming that one of the most iconic images of Buzz Aldrin could only be taken with an artificial light source. So computer graphics experts simulated real-time lighting properties at the Apollo 11 landing site. It turns out that Neil Armstrong's spacesuit reflected the Sun's light and was responsible for illuminating Aldrin in the iconic 1969 photo.

Perhaps the best proof of the Moon landings is the trail of evidence left by the astronauts. The Apollo 11 mission brought Moon rocks back to 135 countries for their scientists to examine, and they have confirmed their lunar origin. The astronauts also planted reflective panels on the surface of the Moon; when other countries shot lasers at them, they pinged back a signal. If the Moon landings were a hoax, researchers from across the globe would have had to have been in on the conspiracy too.

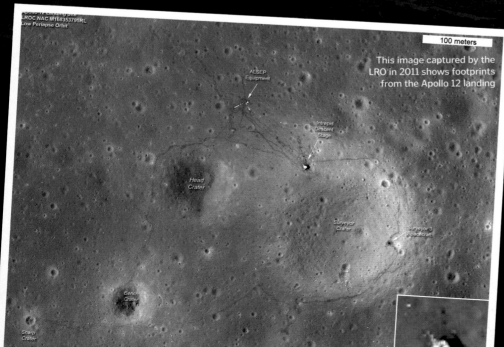

Apollo 12 Landing Site
LROC NAC M168353795RL
Low Periapse Orbit

100 meters

This image captured by the LRO in 2011 shows footprints from the Apollo 12 landing

ALSEP Equipment

Intrepid Descent Stage

Head Crater

Surveyor Crater

Surveyor 3 Spacecraft

Bench Crater

Sharp Crater

Moon conspiracies debunked

"YOU CAN'T SEE THE STARS"

The Moon has no atmosphere, so shouldn't the stars be visible? Like spacesuits, Moon rock reflects sunlight. It is too bright on the surface to see the dim light from distant stars.

"THE ROCKS ARE PROPS"

This rock appears to have the letter 'C' on it, but it's only present in enlarged images, not in the original NASA images, so it's more likely to be a stray hair on the film.

"SHADOWS ARE DIFFERENT LENGTHS"

Some think the inconsistent shadows reveal many light sources, but they can be explained by the rocky, hilly terrain. The landscape of the Moon casts shadows at different lengths.

"THE FLAG IS FLAPPING"

There shouldn't be any wind, but the flag waves as it's planted. It's just the astronauts twisting it to get it into the ground. It stays still later on.

"IT WAS FILMED IN SLOW MOTION"

Were the astronauts held up with wires and filmed in slow motion? Look at the dust — it drops straight down to the ground. On Earth it would form clouds because of the air in the atmosphere.

Contrails only form in certain atmospheric conditions

"PLANES ARE SPRAYING TOXINS OVER US"

If you look up outside you might notice the blue sky strewn with artificial reflective clouds. These telltale streaks of white are called contrails, and they are produced by aircraft exhaust emissions. Contrails form when the hydrocarbon content of jet fuel produces water as a by-product of combustion. The water mixes with cold, wet air and condenses, and it can freeze to form ice crystals. However, some believe that there is a more malevolent undercurrent to the goings-on in the upper troposphere and lower stratosphere.

Most advocates of the so-called 'chemtrails' conspiracy recall seeing fewer and less lingering contrails when they were younger. However, this can be explained by the dramatic increase in air traffic we've seen over the last few decades, as well as cooler exhaust emissions thanks to increased fuel efficiency.

Unsurprisingly, the evidence for chemtrails isn't compelling and remains built on pseudo-scientific principles. Conspiracy theorists' claims range from the idea that government agencies are attempting to turn clouds into spying devices to control our minds, to the notion that they are spraying chemicals to deliberately make us sick.

There is one peer-reviewed paper on the topic, and it doesn't support the outlandish secret spraying scandal. The researchers asked 77 atmospheric scientists to review the data for evidence of chemtrails. Only one scientist said there was a possibility some of it could be evidence, but they also articulated that it wouldn't be the only explanation.

The chemtrail conspiracy theory first emerged shortly after a paper entitled *Weather as a Force Multiplier* was published by the US Air Force in 1996. The article outlined speculations by military researchers about whether the ability to control the weather could be useful in combat. Though the US Air Force have maintained that this was purely hypothetical, it is understandably a chilling thought. Even so, there's nothing up in the air with this one: the scientific data confirms that contrails are completely harmless.

"VACCINES CAUSE AUTISM"

This dangerous myth all started when a fraudulent study led by Dr Andrew Wakefield was published in the highly respected medical journal *The Lancet* in 1998. He studied children diagnosed with autism after receiving the combined vaccination for measles, mumps and rubella (MMR). He claimed that the vaccine caused autism and bowel disorders. Parents quickly stopped vaccinating their children. Another theory falsely implicates the use of thiomersal, a mercury-based vaccine preservative, with autism.

In the years that followed, more rigorous studies found no link between the MMR vaccine and autism: Wakefield was wrong. Ecological studies looked at the numbers of vaccinated children versus the number of children with autism. In Canada, autism rates increased while MMR vaccination rates went down. Sweden and Denmark removed thiomersal from vaccinations in 1992, but autism rates continued to rise. Retrospective cohort studies looked back through medical records to find links. One Danish study analysed over 537,000 children but found no link between their vaccination date and autism diagnosis. Prospective cohort studies followed children after vaccination to see if they went on to develop autism. In Finland doctors found 31 children with symptoms described by Wakefield but none became autistic. Then there was a meta-analysis conducted by Taylor et al that gathered results from more than 1.25 million children. They found no link either. Measles, mumps and rubella are dangerous infections that can cause deafness, meningitis, brain swelling and death. In 2010, *The Lancet* retracted Wakefield's paper, with the UK's General Medical Council striking Wakefield off the medical register for serious professional misconduct in the same year.

The full course of MMR vaccine requires two doses

BAD SCIENCE Why was Wakefield's research eventually discredited?

Statistics
There were only 12 children in Wakefield's study — not enough to draw a firm conclusion.

No control data
The children in Wakefield's study weren't compared to children who hadn't had the MMR vaccine.

Memory
The paper relied on parental anecdotes, which are not a reliable form of evidence.

Vague conclusions
The conclusions made in the paper were speculation and were not based on solid evidence.

VACCINE TIMELINE

1998
Wakefield publishes his paper in *The Lancet*, making a link between the MMR vaccine and autism.

2002
Pediatrics publish the results of a study that used more than 535,000 records and found no link between the MMR vaccine and hospitalisation for autism.

2004
Ten of the 13 original authors retract their support for Wakefield's 1998 paper linking MMR and autism in *The Lancet*.

2010
The General Medical Council remove Wakefield from the UK's medical register. *The Lancet* fully retracts his research.

2014
Meta-analysis completed by Taylor et al gathers data from over 1 million children and finds no link between autism and vaccinations.

2001
The *British Medical Journal* publish a major statistical analysis showing autism diagnosis is rising while MMR coverage stays the same.

2002
The *New England Journal of Medicine* publish the results of a study that tracked over 537,000 children for over seven years and found no link.

2005
Japanese scientists publish their study of over 30,000 children showing a rise in autism diagnosis in Japan after the MMR vaccine was withdrawn in 1993.

2011
The *British Medical Journal* publishes a report by journalist Brian Deer. He reveals that Wakefield had undeclared conflicts of interest and had manipulated evidence.

Crop circles come in all shapes and sizes, from simple circles to complex designs

CONSPIRACIES

TECH

SCIENCE

TRANSPORT

SPACE

ENVIRONMENT

HISTORY

"CLIMATE CHANGE IS A HOAX"

"CROP CIRCLES ARE MADE BY ALIENS"

As giant discs carved among crops, the origins of these elaborate designs have been debated for decades. Some claim that aliens are using fields as notepads in an attempt to communicate with us. Others believe that they are made by human time travellers sent back to warn the present-day population. Others think it could be a strange natural phenomena.

Large proportions of circles occur in southern England, and in recent years patterns have become larger and more detailed. Those who favour a more extraterrestrial explanation believe they are created by spaceships or invisible energy beams from space. Reports of crop stem nodules morphing and elongating have been theorised to be the result of exposure to an

unexplained source of microwave radiation. But, while there is physical evidence of crop circles, their presence has a scientific explanation.

The prevailing theory, which is supported by evidence, is that humans carve the circles. Commonly named 'the circle makers', groups of artists have been observed during their sculpting and even interviewed about their work. It appears the trick is to leave no trace of entering and exiting the fields, which they do by working under the cover of night. Artists have been known to use a length of rope and wooden boards to flatten the crops and form creative shapes. Though aliens aren't responsible for the circles, some of these impressive designs are out of this world.

It goes without saying that climate change is a very hot topic in today's political climate, and while most of us accept that it's a very real challenge, there are some who still refuse to believe it. From those that think the whole idea was invented by some countries to reduce the economical value of others, to those that believe it's simply fake news, the conspiracies about climate change abound.

Climate change itself isn't something new for Earth. Our planet has experienced many fluctuations of global warming and cooling that have been recorded through ice core studies. However, the rapid changes we are witnessing today are believed to be driven by human behaviour. Well, believed by some. President Trump regularly airs his scepticism via Twitter: "Record low temperatures and massive amounts of snow. Where the hell is GLOBAL WARMING?"

Some assume there should be a direct relationship between global warming and their local weather, so by that logic the presence of snow or abnormally cold weather in their hometown must mean that global warming is a lie. But the clue is in the name: the temperature occurs on a *global* scale rather than just on a snow-dusted doorstep. Since the late 19th century the global temperature has risen by 1.1 degrees Celsius, with the rise escalating in the last 35 years to make 2016 the warmest year on record. However, global temperatures are just one of many figures used to illustrate climate change.

Sea levels have risen by about 20 centimetres since the beginning of the 20th century, and since the Industrial Revolution ocean acidity has increased by 30 per cent, causing certain species to relocate as a result. Global warming and climate change might be an inconvenient truth, but they are an unequivocal truth nonetheless.

Why do people believe conspiracies?

Part of it is down to proportionality bias. It is a tendency of the human brain to convince us that big events must have a big cause. Rather than accept the simple explanation, it's somehow easier to believe an elaborate conspiracy.

Another factor is projection bias. We think that other people think like us, and if we're suspicious, or behave suspiciously, we believe that others will be hiding the truth too.

Then there's confirmation bias. We're much more likely to accept evidence that agrees with our existing beliefs than evidence that contradicts us. Once someone gets invested in a conspiracy, they'll become more and more convinced that it's true.

We are more likely to accept evidence if it agrees with beliefs we already have

"THE EARTH IS FLAT"

By around 500 BCE most ancient Greeks believed our planet was round. For a long time before this it was believed to be flat. It was only when we started to map the trajectory of the Sun and the stars and applied mathematics to speculation that we rejected the disc model and accepted the spherical model. You can see the evidence of this curve yourself. Just sit on a clear day and watch a sailing boat as it cruises over the horizon, and you will see it slowly disappear as it dips beneath the horizon and eventually out of sight. This was just one argument made by Aristotle (circa 384–322 BCE), who was possibly the first person to propose a spherical Earth based on physical evidence in around 350 BCE.

So what evidence do modern flat Earth societies have to continue to believe claims that are flat out unsubstantiated? These conspiracy theorists reject the irrefutable evidence of gravity and instead favour the position that we are on a disc that is being pushed upwards through space by a mysterious force called dark energy. They believe that our planet is a disc-shaped world with the Arctic Circle in the middle, with a rotating dome of stars over our heads. Among other absurdities are theories that the Sun is only several hundred kilometres away from us, the Moon is transparent and a giant magnet under the ocean controls the tide.

Perhaps the most outlandish aspect of the flat Earth conspiracy theory is the belief that our planet is surrounded by a huge, 45-metre-high ice wall on the coast of Antarctica that holds our ocean in and prevents us from falling off the planet. Flat Earth conspiracy theorists not only reject the shape of the Earth but also deny the irrefutable evidence of almost all of the scientific evidence underpinning our understanding of physics, mathematics and our origins.

The model of a flat Earth is incorrect and has no scientific support

Level horizon
According to some believers, the Earth must be flat as no matter how high you go, you never have to look down at the horizon.

Disc-shaped Earth
Flat Earthers claim that an ice wall prevents us from falling off our disc-shaped world into oblivion.

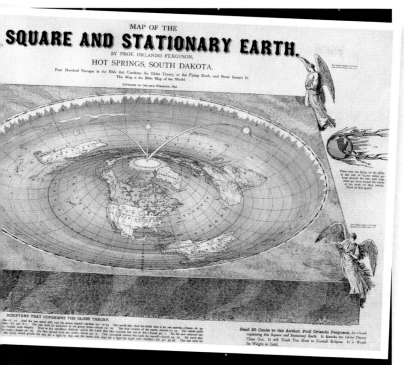

MAP OF THE
SQUARE AND STATIONARY EARTH.
BY PROF. ORLANDO FERGUSON,
HOT SPRINGS, SOUTH DAKOTA.

Orlando Ferguson's 1893 map argues against the idea of a spherical Earth

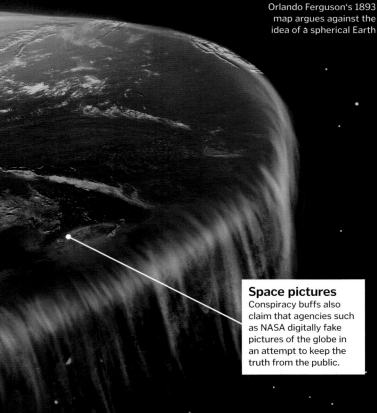

Space pictures
Conspiracy buffs also claim that agencies such as NASA digitally fake pictures of the globe in an attempt to keep the truth from the public.

"Theorists favour the position that we are on a disc that is being pushed upwards by a force called dark energy"

Five reasons why we know the Earth is round

1 PHOTOGRAPHY FROM SPACE

Countless photographs taken by satellites, probes and from the ISS show our Earth as a beautiful globe, which is unarguably the greatest piece of evidence that the world is not flat.

2 LUNAR ECLIPSE SHADOWS

During a lunar eclipse, the Earth is placed between the Moon and Sun. The shadow cast by our Earth is visibly round as a result of its spherical shape.

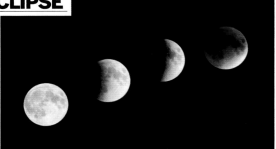

3 DIFFERENT VISIBLE CONSTELLATIONS

From a flat Earth all the stars would look the same no matter where in the world you were standing, but this isn't the case — different constellations can be seen in different parts of the globe.

4 WE CAN SEE FURTHER WITH ALTITUDE

The higher up you are the further you will see. This is a result of the Earth's curvature. On a flat Earth, elevation would not make a difference and curvature would thereby not occur.

5 TIME ZONES

If Earth was flat the Sun's light would be equally distributed everywhere; similar to placing a plate beneath a desk lamp. This would mean we wouldn't have any time zones, or day and night.

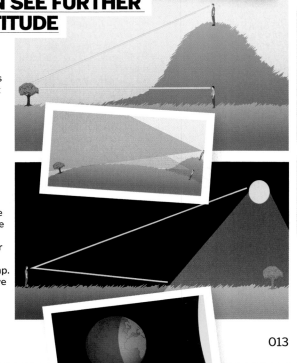

We uncover some of the biggest falsehoods in technology

"VIDEO GAMES MAKE PEOPLE MORE VIOLENT"

The idea that absorbing violent content through media encourages our own violent thoughts and actions isn't new. In fact, it's been around since violent scenes first appeared on the silver screen in the 1970s, with parents and conservative groups fearful of the negative impact viewing such things could have. The swift transformation of video games in the decades that followed, from family friendly titles such as *Super Mario* to the R rated *Grand Theft Auto* series, did nothing to allay their concerns.

Suddenly young adults, rather than just watch a person harm another in gruesome ways on the screen, could take control of an avatar and commit such virtual crimes themselves. In *Grand Theft Auto* — a famous example of such a game — players could even shoot or simply run down innocent bystanders. While these games were designed purely for entertainment, gamers found their appetites for on-screen violence ever increasing so scientists decided to step in and investigate their potential impact.

Several scientific findings have been published on the topic, and at first glance it seems like bad news for gamers. In a laboratory setting, numerous studies asserted the same conclusion: exposure to violence could invoke such behaviour in the viewer. However, a more recent comprehensive survey released in 2014 used crime statistics to debunk this view. The researchers compared rates of youth violence against consumption of violent video games and discovered the two were inversely related. The study had shown that youths were becoming less inclined to commit criminal violence with the rise of violent video games.

"IT'S BEST TO LET BATTERIES RUN OUT BEFORE RECHARGING"

This battery myth, which supposedly helps to extend a device's lifespan, is a notorious example of an incorrect piece of information that seems to endure even when it becomes outdated. And, if we're able to admit it, most of us have probably shared this 'helpful' tip with others, unaware that our advice will actually harm their product's battery life rather than help it.

Most modern batteries, including all those used in our precious Apple iPhones and MacBooks, make use of lithium-ion batteries. Compare these to traditional battery technologies and you'll find that they are claimed to charge faster, last longer and, most importantly for addressing this myth, charge best in short, 'topping-up' bursts. Apple measures their battery lifespans in cycles, with one cycle being equal to 100 per cent discharge, but that doesn't mean that you should completely drain your battery before plugging in your device. Instead, it's best to split a charge cycle across multiple charges.

In fact, most tech advisors suggest never letting your phone battery get too low, nor too high. Not that a full-charge will be overly damaging, but consistently leaving your device plugged in until it has stored every last drop of energy can reduce its lifespan in the long term. Instead, take advantage of your device's inbuilt charging design, which will likely be a 'quick-charge' to 80 per cent and 'trickle-charge' from 80 to 100 per cent. This design ensures that you can get power back quickly but stops your device from overcharging. So discard this common myth and stop waiting for your bar to empty before filling it up. Instead, keep your bar in the green, and charge from 40 per cent to 80 per cent for the most efficient battery life.

Contrary to popular belief, letting a modern battery's charge fall too low is damaging for its longevity

"PLANNED OBSOLESCENCE MAKES YOUR PHONE SLOW DOWN"

Although Macs can get viruses, they're not as common as in PCs

Conspiracy theories can be fun to discuss, but they become so much more fascinating when they contain a grain of truth. Such is the case with 'planned obsolescence', a manufacturer's tactic that had been in play for decades before the term had even been invented.

In essence, planned obsolescence is a deliberate ploy by the manufacturer to limit their product's lifespan so the consumer is forced to repeatedly pay to replace it. And to the chagrin of today's manufacturers, conspiracy theorists often point to the infamous 'Phoebus cartel' of light bulb makers, who in the 1920s planned to do exactly that. But as technology has developed, attention has shifted away from light bulbs and onto smartphones, with recent theories suggesting that tech giants, such as Apple, restrict the performance of older devices in order to encourage consumers to purchase newer, more expensive models.

As this idea has inspired such widespread belief, software company Futuremark decided to put iPhones, old and new, to the test. They assessed each model's performance every month for 18 months and found that their performance was maintained. The slowed-down performance owners had been reporting was more likely due to installing software updates released with the new models, which are designed to work optimally with the newest units.

However, in December 2017 Apple announced that their iOS software does in fact slow the performance of older iPhone models in order to preserve battery life. Old lithium-ion batteries don't hold their charge as well as new ones, so the programmed slow down is a compromise to stop the battery draining too quickly and to prevent random shut downs, which would otherwise be frustrating for users.

So is the slowing performance a scheme by manufacturers to boost profits? Not exactly.

Does their approach to software updates render old models obsolete? Eventually.

"MACS CANNOT GET VIRUSES"

Lots of us long for a Mac of our own, with their sleek design, sophisticated hardware and intuitive software catapulting them to the top of many wish lists. Add to that the common notion that they're immune to viruses, and they almost sound like the perfect machine. Only, as more users are discovering, Macs are susceptible to viruses, spyware and other types of malware just like PCs.

However, this myth hasn't arisen from nowhere. Macs do encounter much less malicious software (often abbreviated to malware) than Microsoft PCs, which has led to their inflated reputation. A primary reason for this is simply that there are more people using PCs therefore making them the obvious target for opportunistic hackers. Today, with a growing number of Mac users around, hackers have more incentive to design viruses for Macs. However, by their very design, Macs are much better equipped to deal with possible threats, with their inbuilt security measures capable of restricting unknown applications from installing on the system. But, there is no computer that is completely secure.

Light bulb manufacturers have been revealed as exploiters of 'planned obsolescence' in the past

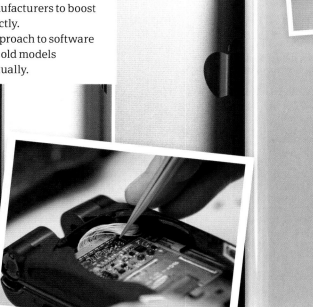

"Macs are susceptible to viruses just like PCs"

015

Camera advertisements often revolve around megapixels, but they are a measure of quantity not quality

Shuffle play prevents tracks from repeating, making it distinct from a random play feature

"SHUFFLE ON MUSIC PLAYERS IS COMPLETELY RANDOM"

Shuffle playlists are great when we're in an indecisive mood. Not sure what music to listen to? No problem. Just click 'shuffle' and the device will randomly choose songs from a playlist or library for you to listen to. Or will it? At least in the case of the music streaming service Spotify, the answer is no, it's not quite as random as you might expect.

Instead, they've designed an algorithm to make your shuffle playlist *seem* more random than a truly random playlist would be. And as bizarre as that sounds, it makes sense when we consider that humans are very good at making patterns — even when there aren't any. The algorithm attempts to circumvent a human invention known as 'gambler's fallacy', which explains our tendency to think that if a coin has landed on heads five times in a row, then it's likely to land on tails on the next toss. But really, every time we flip a coin, the chances of it landing on heads or tails is equal (well, more or less… see page 22).

When we hear an artist on shuffle appear twice in quick succession, we instinctively wonder how the playlist can be random if the same artist has cropped up twice so soon. So Spotify have introduced the algorithm to separate an artist's songs in order to cater to what we perceive to be random.

Music streaming services such as Spotify use algorithms to make their playlists seem more random

"MORE MEGAPIXELS MEANS BETTER PHOTOGRAPHS"

Like many tech-related myths, presenting megapixels as the sole determinant of image quality is a result of misleading marketing campaigns. And unfortunately for consumers, all the big phone- and camera-creating manufacturers have hopped onboard with this advertising strategy. But more doesn't necessarily mean better, and in some cases, more megapixels can even make your photographs worse!

Digital cameras — unlike their predecessors that captured images using light-sensitive film — build images through pixels, which each process a small fraction of light caught by the camera's sensors. With more pixels comes more units to capture incoming light, increasing the camera's resolution and providing images with more detail. This can be helpful when making large prints or zooming in on images, but otherwise you'll notice little difference between a seven- and ten-megapixel camera, for example.

It's also important to note that there are many more factors at play than just megapixels, with the camera lens, sensor, flash and software all being important elements. Plus, with more megapixels comes the requirement for more light to accurately capture the image, so a higher megapixel camera can produce lower-quality images than one with less megapixels when the other components are not up to scratch.

"MAGNETS CAN ERASE YOUR DATA"

You may have seen a piece of movie sabotage involving the use of a magnet to erase the contents of a hard drive, or you may have simply been told to keep your devices well clear of them, but this danger is largely mythical. For forms of flash memory that use solid state drives, magnetism will have no effect whatsoever, so your laptop, smartphone and USB stick are probably perfectly safe.

For hard disc drives, however, the danger is partially real. These devices create a binary code using polar alignments on the magnetic parts, so a strong enough magnet could alter the polarity and ruin the data. Myth confirmed? Not quite, as the magnet would have to be as strong as an MRI machine to have any impact. So unless your devices are going to be exposed to a super-magnet, they'll be safe.

A magnet as powerful as an MRI scanner could destroy data on a hard disc drive

"QWERTY IS THE MOST EFFICIENT KEYBOARD LAYOUT AVAILABLE"

Keyboards beginning from the top left with the characters Q-W-E-R-T-Y have become ubiquitous with modern computers. And as many of us find this keyboard style easy to use, it seems appropriate that the alphabet is arranged in this way simply because it's the most efficient. However, the QWERTY layout is actually a relic from the typewriter era.

Originally, typewriters were arranged in alphabetical order, but as commonly used letters were placed next to each other this caused the machine to jam if these letters were struck in close succession, as the bars that pressed against the paper would collide. QWERTY was the answer to this issue, so common keys were placed further apart from one another.

However, the 'Dvorak' and 'Colemak' arrangements are arguably more efficient, as commonly used characters are placed where they can easily be reached. But given you would have to retrain your brain and fingers, most of us will probably continue to stick with QWERTY.

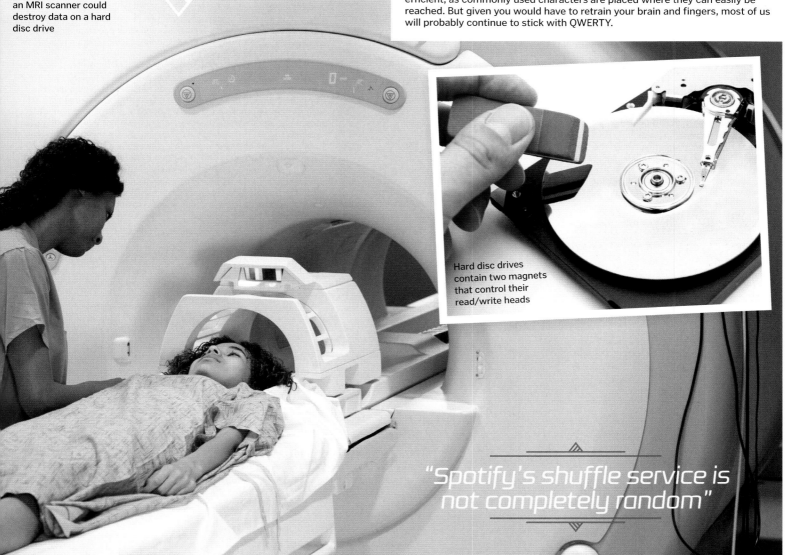

Hard disc drives contain two magnets that control their read/write heads

"Spotify's shuffle service is not completely random"

CONSPIRACIES

TECH

SCIENCE

TRANSPORT

SPACE

ENVIRONMENT

HISTORY

We put eight of the most persistent science myths under the microscope

The first commercial chewing gum was made and sold in 1848 by John B Curtis

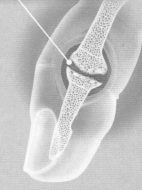

Barium can be used to find blockages in the intestine, including swallowed gum

"COIN FLIPS ARE 50:50"

If there's one thing that we know for sure, it's that a series of coin tosses will come out half heads and half tails. Wrong. Coin flips aren't completely independent. True, the coin doesn't know what side it landed on last time, so if you got five heads in a row, you aren't overdue a tails. But the side that faces upwards when you make the flip influences the side it'll land on.

Researchers from Stanford University and University of California, Santa Cruz watched coin flips with a high-speed camera. They found that if you flip a coin head-side up you have a 51 per cent chance of catching it head-side up. And, for some people, the chance can be as high as 60 per cent depending on exactly how they flip the coin. What's more, if you spin the coin, the lightest side will face up more often than the heaviest. This tends to be tails, but it depends on the exact coin you use. The advantage is tiny but well worth knowing about if you're betting on a coin toss.

If you flip a coin head-side up, it's more likely to land head-side up

"IT TAKES SEVEN YEARS TO DIGEST CHEWING GUM"

It can take on average between one to three days for food to go all the way through your digestive system, but legend has it that gum stays in there for seven years! Luckily for any accidental gum swallowers, this simply isn't true. So what exactly does happen to chewing gum when we swallow it?

The chewy part of chewing gum is made of tough stuff — a natural or synthetic rubber base that even the digestive system can't break down, able to withstand the stomach's acid and the intestines' digestive enzymes. But most other components, including sweeteners and flavourings, can be broken down. This means the body can deal with it, so the gum will eventually move towards the exit in a few days. If you swallow something smaller than two centimetres in diameter, chances are it'll be able to squeeze out. And gum has the added benefit of being soft.

There have been rare reports of children with gummed-up intestines, but they had swallowed vast quantities of the sticky stuff. Even so, chewing gum has no nutritional benefit, and can be a choking hazard, so you are still advised to spit it out.

"CRACKING KNUCKLES WILL CAUSE ARTHRITIS"

Knuckle cracking involves pulling apart the joints by stretching or bending them, which decreases the pressure in the fluid between them. This causes dissolved gases in the fluid to form bubbles, which then burst with a characteristic crack. Legend has it that this causes osteoarthritis, where the cartilage covering the ends of the bones becomes thin and roughens. But this legend isn't true.

In 1998, Dr Donald L Unger wrote a letter to the editor of *Arthritis and Rheumatology*. He had been cracking the knuckles of his left hand at least twice a day for 50 years, with his right hand acting as the control. He had compared both hands for evidence of arthritis and found none, but he did confess that his study wasn't enough to debunk the myth.

However, a larger study later appeared in the *Journal of the American Board of Family Medicine*. The team quizzed 215 people aged 50–89 about their knuckle-cracking habits and looked at X-rays of their hands. The result? There was no difference between those who cracked and those who didn't.

Healthy joint
The joint is surrounded by a capsule of synovial fluid. The bones have a thin layer of cartilage, which acts like a shock absorber.

Erosive osteoarthritis
The cartilage has completely disappeared. The bones rub against each other and wear away.

Moderate osteoarthritis
The cartilage has become thin and gradually roughens. The synovium makes extra fluid, which causes swelling.

Osteoarthritis is caused by wear to the cartilage that covers the joints

"YOU ONLY USE TEN PER CENT OF YOUR BRAIN"

While the human species is already pretty smart, could we be even smarter? The old saying goes that we only use ten per cent of our brains. So just imagine what we could do if we kicked the other 90 per cent into gear. Not much more, as it turns out. The ten per cent figure is a myth.

We don't know exactly where the myth came from, but it may have started as a misinterpretation of early experiments on brains. The first cause could be the fact that during brain scans, not all parts of the brain light up, possibly leading early experts to assume that the darker areas were inactive. On top of this, there is the fact that people can survive damage to certain parts of the brain following a trauma such as a stroke.

We each have around 86 billion nerve cells, or neurons, in our brains. Each one can have up to 100,000 dendrites, which are branches that help neurons to make connections to each other. Just by reading this page, you're using almost every part of your brain. Your brainstem is taking care of your heart rate and breathing. Your cerebellum is keeping you

balanced. Your occipital lobe is handling the input from your eyes. And your temporal, parietal and frontal lobes are working together to decode the words. All this brain activity, needs energy; up to 20 per cent of the body's total in fact. That's a lot for using just ten per cent of the brain.

If this still isn't enough, around half of your brain isn't made of neurons but glial cells. The word is Greek for 'glue', and these cells sit between the neurons, providing support and protection. Then there are the astroglia, which help maintain chemical balance; oligodendrocytes, which insulate neurons; and the microglia that repair damage, fight infection and clean up debris. These cells are constantly active, blowing the ten per cent figure out of the water.

> "We each have around 86 billion nerve cells in our brains"

Neurons in the brain (red) are supported by star-shaped astrocytes (green)

"A PENNY DROPPED FROM A SKYSCRAPER COULD KILL SOMEONE"

Coins tumble through the air, limiting their top speed

There's no need to fear for your life the next time you pass through the shadow of a skyscraper — pennies dropped from the rooftops aren't going to pierce your skull. Intrepid investigators have put this myth to the test in ingenious ways, and it's been well and truly busted.

University of Virginia physics professor Louis Bloomfield was so confident that the myth was false that he sent a penny-loaded helium balloon into the sky. The pennies dropped like leaves in the air, buffeted by the wind. The faster they fell, the more air resistance they experienced. Pennies are too small and flat to be a danger, only reaching speeds of around 40.2 kilometres per hour. At some point the downward force of gravity balances the upward force of air resistance, and the pennies can't fall any faster.

According to the *MythBusters* team, a penny dropped from the top of the Empire State Building might collide with the pavement at 103.6 kilometres per hour. So they made a gun that could fire pennies at that speed. Although their test dummy may have suffered a little damage, when they turned on each other they were not harmed. According to Professor Bloomfield, if the coins fell in a vacuum they'd be much more dangerous, reaching a speed of 335.7 kilometres per hour. But even then they wouldn't penetrate the skull.

However, in an interview with *Life's Little Mysteries*, he warned against ballpoint pens. The shape of these is more bullet-like, and if they come down straight they could get close to 335.7 kilometres per hour in the air, so the pointy end could do a lot more damage.

The average sneeze travels at a speed of 163.9 kilometres per hour

"SNEEZING WITH YOUR EYES OPEN WOULD MAKE YOUR EYES POP OUT"

People shut their eyes when they sneeze, but it's not to prevent them from bulging out of their heads. We sneeze to clear irritants from our airways, and closing our eyes stops the same irritants from getting straight back in. It happens automatically, but if you do keep your eyes open it's highly unlikely that anything bad will happen.

In 1882, *The New York Times* reported a burst eyeball following a sneeze, and it's true that straining can rupture blood vessels. A powerful sneeze or excessive coughing can cause a bleed in the eye. These injuries normally heal without any need for treatment, and they can happen whether your eyes are open or closed.

"We sneeze to clear irritants from our airways"

The Coriolis effect isn't strong enough to affect household drains

Hurricanes spin anti-clockwise in the Northern Hemisphere and clockwise in the Southern

"WATER DRAINS IN THE OPPOSITE ROTATION IN THE SOUTHERN HEMISPHERE"

Earth is always spinning. It rotates from west to east, completing a full turn every 24 hours, and this causes something known as the Coriolis effect. Earth is a sphere, and it's wider at the equator than it is at the poles. Therefore, for the whole planet to spin around in the same amount of time, the ground at the equator has to spin faster than the ground at the poles.

If you were able to stand at the equator and throw a ball northwards towards your friend in the UK, it would appear to curve to the right because they are moving slower and have not caught up, while you conserve momentum. But if you were in the North Pole and threw a ball towards the UK, again it would curve to the right, but because the UK is moving faster than at the pole, your friends are now ahead of the ball.

Back on terra firma, the effect is that liquids, including those in the air, deflect as they move. You can watch it happening in the spin of hurricanes, which turn in different directions in the Northern and Southern hemispheres. But this effect isn't strong enough to affect water draining from our sinks: the Earth just isn't moving fast enough.

"HAIR AND NAILS CONTINUE TO GROW AFTER YOU DIE"

Medical students and morticians might notice cadavers with fresh stubble, but there isn't a mysterious life force inside the follicles. It may look like new cells are growing at the roots, but appearances can be deceiving. After death, the body starts to dry out and, as skin loses moisture, it shrinks. What looks like new growth is just hair and nails that were once hidden underneath being revealed.

Many of our cells do stay alive longer than us. Studies looking at the genes of animals in the four days after they died showed that many cells activated automated stress responses after death. Stem cells in particular fight to survive as long as possible.

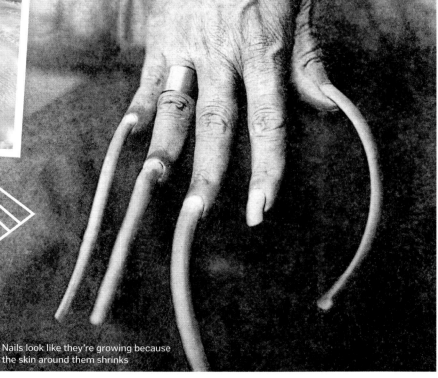

Nails look like they're growing because the skin around them shrinks

From airborne bugs to petrol pump pyrotechnics, we uncover some transport truths

"THE BERMUDA TRIANGLE IS DANGEROUS"

Legend has it that the subtropical Bermuda Triangle region of the western North Atlantic is the site of hundreds of tragic and unexplained disasters. The stories surrounding the fateful disappearance of planes and ships in the area between Miami, Bermuda and Puerto Rico are often centred around the supernatural.

There are fanciful tales describing rifts in space-time sucking in unsuspecting sea-faring travellers, or the area being haunted by the souls of African people enslaved by the British. Some theories have even suggested that aliens might be responsible for the eerie events. However, the truth is much less paranormal.

The foundations of this myth are rooted in the time of Christopher Columbus, who reported witnessing a great flame of fire (likely a meteor) crashing into the ocean as he sailed through the triangle during his first voyage to the New World. Later, in the 20th century, the naval cargo ship USS Cyclops went missing in the Bermuda Triangle, along with the 300 or so people onboard. No remains of the ship or crew were found, and no distress call had been made despite the ship having the equipment to do so.

One of the most mysterious events since then involved the small ship Witchcraft. In December 1967, Witchcraft hit something apparently minor within 1.6 kilometres of the shore. Calmly, the experienced captain onboard, Dan Burack, said they needed to be towed but it wasn't an emergency, and he'd fire a flare to indicate his position. Assistance arrived within less than 20 minutes, but he was nowhere to be found and neither was his boat or crew. Burack was a cautious yachtsman and had attached a floatation device to make the boat virtually unsinkable, so even if the hull had been ruptured and the boat flooded, part of it would remain above water. Yet no debris was ever found, despite searching over 63,000 square kilometres.

There are countless other stories, some steeped in folklore and more embellished than others. But statistically there have not been more wrecks in this area. That doesn't mean that the Bermuda Triangle is the safest of waters though. It's known that storms, reefs and the Gulf Stream can cause navigational challenges, but these mysterious goings-on are mostly due to the sheer amount of traffic going through, human error and bad weather, plus the heightened publicity given to accidents within the area.

BERMUDA (U.K.)

The truth is clouded
Meteorologists now think that unusual hexagonal clouds above the triangle create 'air bombs' full of wind that are able to bring down a plane or send a ship to the bottom of the Atlantic.

Atlantic Ocean

BAHAMAS

Tropic of Cancer

Miami

An ocean of danger?
The Bermuda Triangle covers roughly 1.3 million square kilometres of ocean off the southeastern tip of Florida.

Havana

CUBA

DOMINICAN REPUBLIC

HAITI

PUERTO RICO (U.S.)

Considering accidents as a percentage of the ships that pass through the Bermuda Triangle, it is no more dangerous than anywhere else

BELIZE

HO

The Bermuda Triangle is home to many myths surrounding stories that have become distorted over the years

Nicaragua

VENEZUELA

"PLANES DUMP TOILET WASTE IN FLIGHT"

It is impossible to intentionally dump waste from an airplane mid-flight

Visiting an aircraft toilet is generally an unpleasant affair. It's difficult enough to squeeze into the cramped room and navigate onto the seat, without the additional concern of what may be about to be unceremoniously dumped into the sea. There have always been rumours concerning the fate of waste at altitude – that it is to be jettisoned from the aircraft, but it turns out that this is actually impossible to do.

This is because airline toilets use either closed waste systems (which operate in a similar way to a house toilet) or a more modern vacuum waste system. Both store the sewage in holding tanks and require access to a valve on the outside of the plane to be emptied.

However, there are cases where waste has seeped out of an aircraft accidentally because of a leak in the tank. The waste becomes immediately frozen, along with the blue waste treatment liquid. This grisly frozen mixture is known as blue ice. Though generally blue ice will collect on the outside of the aircraft and remain there until the plane has landed, there are occasions where it can come loose.

Thankfully, most will melt and evaporate before hitting the ground, or an unlucky passerby, but occasionally the pungent snowball will remain intact. There have been verified reports of people and property being hit with blue ice, but it has never been intentional.

"AIRBAGS KILL MORE PEOPLE THAN THEY SAVE"

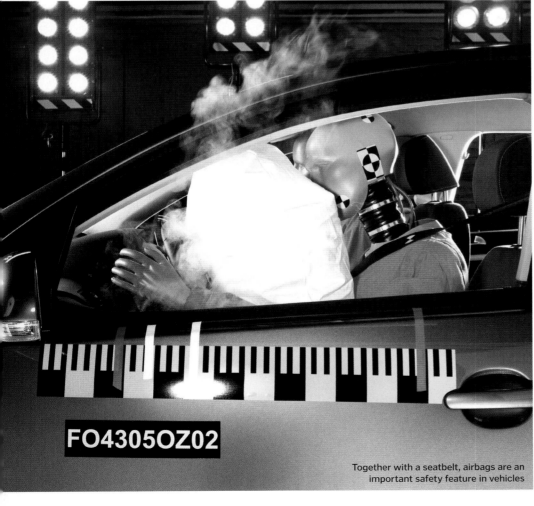

FO4305OZ02

Together with a seatbelt, airbags are an important safety feature in vehicles

There's no doubt that airbags save lives by reducing the impact of a crash, but there is still a rumbling of urban myths surrounding these road safety devices. You might have heard that airbags kill more people than they save, but this is incorrect. They generally only cause injury if they're used incorrectly.

The National Highway Traffic Safety Administration estimate that between 1987-2015, a total of 44,869 lives were saved. While, between 1990-2008, more than 290 fatalities had occurred. So, unless you ignore safety guidelines, it is much riskier to drive a car that's not fitted with airbags than one that is.

"MOBILE PHONES CAN BRING A PLANE DOWN"

Have you ever noticed that sometimes, usually just before your phone rings, your speakers start emitting a static sound? That's cellular interference, and it's quite annoying. It's even more annoying if it's being blasted through your headset when you're a member of the flight crew trying to organise irritated passengers while simultaneously preparing to launch an 80-ton plane 12,000 metres into the air.

Not being allowed to use your phone onboard actually has nothing to do with potentially causing a crash: it's more due to the risk of this cellular interference sound distracting flight crew. There is almost no risk of causing a plane crash because you were using your phone, but aviation authorities understandably choose to err on the side of caution.

Modern aircraft have electronics that are designed to shield them from interference from cellular communication. It's estimated that at least half of all phones are not switched onto flight mode, and there remains no known flight that was adversely affected by this kind of interference. So while you could send those last few Snapchat selfies as your flight takes off, for the sake of the crew, it's probably best not to risk it.

Mobile phones may be annoying on flights, but they won't bring a plane down

"THE TITANIC WAS KNOWN AS 'UNSINKABLE'"

Submerged nearly four kilometres beneath the surface of the icy North Atlantic Ocean lies the red-rusted remains of the magnificent ocean liner the RMS Titanic. This iconic passenger vessel is remembered as the unsinkable ship, but did anyone at the time really believe this to be true? Evidence suggests that while passengers and crew did feel they were aboard an exceptionally safe vessel, there had been no advertising of the liner as being 'unsinkable'.

This phrasing only came from the White Star Line after the Titanic had sunk. When reports of the sinking ship reached America on the morning of the 15 April 1912, Philip Franklin (the vice president of the company) announced, "There is no danger that Titanic will sink. The boat is unsinkable and nothing but inconvenience will be suffered by the passengers."

Previous to the sinking of the Titanic, the only known record of someone saying the ship was unsinkable came from a crewmember to calm the nerves of the passenger Mrs Sylvia Caldwell. It's reported he said to her, "God himself could not sink this ship!" The belief that the Titanic was ever seen as the unsinkable ship is a result of latter-day myth making and sensationalism.

The Titanic was never officially described as unsinkable

The ill-fated Titanic had been undisturbed until it was rediscovered in 1985

© Getty; NOAA; Pixabay

024

It might not seem like a nice thought, but the air on a plane is actually cleaner than the air in your office

"RECIRCULATED AIR INSIDE PLANES SPREADS DISEASE"

Nothing says uncomfortable like being trapped inside a confined space with only questionable airplane food and the thought that you're breathing the same continuously recirculated air for the next few hours. You become very aware of the amount of people who are coughing, sneezing and spluttering their way through the aircraft, convinced you will quickly succumb to the sniffles.

It might feel like you're breathing in air saturated with germs, but modern aircraft now have exceptionally powerful systems that use HEPA filters to catch up to 99.97 per cent of airborne microbes. The air is also filtered and recirculated approximately once every two to four minutes. In fact, it's probably cleaner than the air in your office, which is usually only refreshed about 12 times an hour.

The supply of fresh air in a plane isn't lacking either, with 50 per cent of the cabin supply being crisp air from outside. This air is drawn into the plane continuously via compressor stages in the jet's engines. So the next time you're on a flight, while there might not be much you can do about the person kicking your seat, at least you can breathe easy about the air quality.

"USING YOUR PHONE AT THE PETROL STATION COULD CAUSE AN EXPLOSION"

Mobile phones have been held accountable for causing horrific accidents, but much like the stories of crashing planes, exploding petrol stations are also a myth. There is absolutely no scientific evidence to suggest that emitted radiation from a mobile phone can ignite gasoline vapours, but the rumour was propagated with the best of intentions.

Phone manufacturers started this by printing warnings about phone use near gasoline in user manuals, and in response to this, oil companies reacted with caution, with both industries working together to enforce

Using your mobile phone at a petrol station will not cause it to explode

something they felt would protect people. But, once evidence had come to light to disprove the fire theory, petrol stations that chose to keep the 'phones off' rule did so because they're an unwanted distraction, rather than a danger.

Despite having over 2,200 people onboard, the Titanic only carried 20 lifeboats

A fire in the boiler room before launch is thought to have weakened the ship's hull

TITANIC

We pick apart some of the most common misconceptions in the cosmos

The sensation of being in space can make it feel like there's no gravity

Asteroids very rarely collide in space, but it's probably spectacular when they do

Travelling through the asteroid belt would not be as exciting as you might think

"THE ASTEROID BELT IS FULL OF ASTEROIDS"

Blame *Star Wars* for this one. In *The Empire Strikes Back*, Han and co weave their way through an asteroid belt in the Millennium Falcon, dodging flying rocks all over the place, against the odds. It was a great scene, sure, but the science was lacking. The problem is that asteroids just aren't that close together. They're really, really far apart, and flying between them would be a breeze. In the asteroid belt between the orbits of Mars and Jupiter, you'd be hard-pressed to even see one asteroid from the surface of another.

Scientists estimate the main asteroid belt contains between 1.1 and 1.9 million asteroids larger than one kilometre in diameter, and millions of smaller ones. Most known asteroids orbit in this main region, and on average each sizeable asteroid is at least several million kilometres away from another, with the chances of a collision being about one in 1 billion. Could we assume that in a galaxy far, far away, they've found an asteroid belt that's much more tightly packed? Absolutely. But in ours, this scene would have been a lot less exciting.

"THERE'S ZERO GRAVITY IN ORBIT"

Perhaps the most common misconception about space concerns what space actually is. A lot of people seem to think that when you launch a rocket straight upwards, you eventually reach a point where you start floating. That's why the astronauts on the International Space Station (ISS) appear weightless, right?

Well, we're afraid that's just not true. The reason astronauts on the ISS appear to be floating is because they're in constant free fall towards Earth. In the late 17th century, Isaac Newton first published his thought experiment to demonstrate his concept. He suggested that if you fired a cannonball horizontally from the surface of Earth — at greater and greater speeds — the ball would not hit the Earth but instead orbit the planet. That's basically what's happening on the ISS. They're moving so fast (over 28,000 kilometres per hour) that they constantly fall towards the Earth. As a result, they're in constant free fall and appear to experience weightlessness.

In fact, at an altitude ranging between 370–460 kilometres above the Earth's surface, the ISS still experiences 90 per cent of Earth's gravity. Everything in orbit experiences the pull of our planet, it's just that they move so fast sideways that it seems like they are weightless. So, the next time you see footage of astronauts floating around, just remember they're not in zero gravity. They're actually constantly falling, but thanks to the extremely low friction of the upper atmosphere, their spacecraft never slows down, so they never fall to Earth.

Astronauts on the ISS can have a great time in the microgravity environment

"BLACK HOLES SUCK EVERYTHING IN"

Contrary to popular belief, black holes are not cosmic vacuum cleaners that suck up everything in their vicinity. In fact, they behave not that differently from a star at first. It's when you get close that things start to get weird.

First, let's back up. A black hole forms when the centre of a massive star goes supernova, leaving behind a dense core that collapses in on itself. These are known as stellar mass black holes and, as their name suggests, they're actually quite similar in mass to a star. If the Sun was substituted by a black hole of equal mass, all the planets currently orbiting the Sun would continue on their orbits as they are now and would not instantly be pulled in. But the Sun is not massive enough to ever evolve into a black hole.

At the heart of our galaxy is a supermassive black hole, known as Sagittarius A*, and we see these at the centre of almost every massive galaxy. Again, these black holes clearly don't suck everything in. Some, in more distant galaxies, are surrounded by a quasar — a superheated accretion disc of gas and dust — and some can fire jets.

But there is a point beyond which black holes behave quite strangely. At the edge of its inner core, which can be just a few kilometres across, you'll find the event horizon. This is where the gravitational pull is so intense that nothing — not even light — can escape. At this point, you could probably say that the black hole was sucking you in. What happens next is anyone's guess, however, because what goes in never comes out.

Try and stay inside your spacesuit if you can

"YOU'D EXPLODE WITHOUT A SPACESUIT"

Contrary to what some films might have you believe, taking your suit off in space won't cause you to immediately explode. Yes, your outlook isn't great, but it might not be as dramatic as some think. The first thing that would happen is you'd lose consciousness after about 15 seconds due to a lack of oxygen after your body has used up the oxygen in your blood. Before this happens, you would have needed to breathe out as much air from your lungs as possible, otherwise that oxygen will rupture your lung tissue.

Next up you've got ebullism, where the drop in pressure (spacesuits are like mini spacecraft, remember) causes gas bubbles to form inside your body fluids. A test subject accidentally exposed to a vacuum in 1965 reported that he also started to feel saliva on his tongue boiling due to the drop in pressure. So after a few minutes you'd be in pretty serious trouble, and while you might not explode, you probably don't want to stay outside for too long.

Black holes aren't as dangerous and deadly as is commonly thought

Supermassive black holes are thought to be at the centre of nearly every large galaxy

"Black holes are not cosmic vacuum cleaners"

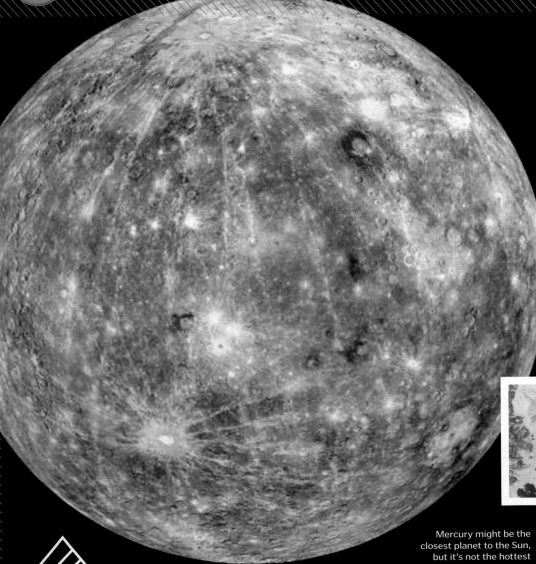

Mercury might be the closest planet to the Sun, but it's not the hottest

"THE GREAT WALL OF CHINA IS VISIBLE FROM SPACE"

More specifically, this myth claims that the Great Wall of China is the only human-made object visible from space. We're sorry to burst your bubble but this simply isn't true, although it does depend on what you count as space. Even from low-Earth orbit (around 160 kilometres up), the wall is not visible to the naked eye. It's just too thin, and the colours don't stand out much from the surrounding landscape. On the ISS, it is barely visible using a camera, and even then only under perfect conditions, but it is certainly not visible from the Moon.

However, you can see other evidence of humanity from the ISS with the naked eye, such as cities in the day and night, as well as airports, dams, bridges and even the pyramids. The official boundary of space is 100 kilometres up, but even from here you'd struggle to see the five-to-ten-meter-wide Great Wall unaided.

The Great Wall is extremely long but not that wide and thus very hard to spot

"THE SUN IS YELLOW"

Think the Sun is yellow? Think again... sort of. The Sun emits all wavelengths of visible light, from violet to red. This means that it would appear white if you could view it with the naked eye in space. However, each colour corresponds to a different temperature, with yellow-green light of 550 nanometres emanating from about 5,700 degrees Celsius. From Earth the Sun appears yellow because the longer-wavelength yellow light is less easily scattered by our atmosphere than shorter-wavelength colours like blue and violet.

The Sun might seem yellow to us, but appearances can be deceiving

"MERCURY IS THE HOTTEST PLANET"

Mercury is the closest planet to the Sun, so surely it should be the hottest planet, right? Well, not quite, and the reason why is rather interesting. The hottest planet in the Solar System is actually Venus, with an average surface temperature of 462 degrees Celsius. But, Mercury reaches highs of 'only' 427 degrees Celsius.

The reason for this difference is that Venus, unlike Mercury, has a thick atmosphere. Instead, Mercury possesses a thin exosphere made up of atoms blasted off its surface by solar wind and micrometeoroids. While Mercury heats up in direct sunlight, things get hotter on Venus, where the mainly carbon dioxide atmosphere traps the Sun's heat in a runaway greenhouse effect.

Scientists think that Venus may once have actually had shallow-liquid water oceans and habitable surface temperatures, but exposure to sunlight caused the ocean to evaporate, and with no water vapour remaining, the planet's atmosphere has thickened and its temperatures have risen.

Venus is the hottest planet in our Solar System thanks to its thick atmosphere

"THE MOON HAS A DARK SIDE"

It might seem like the Moon has a dark side, but actually the Moon has cycles just like Earth does. The reason this myth pervades is because from Earth we can only see one side of the Moon as it's gravitationally (or tidally) locked to our planet.

There is a far side of the Moon that we never see, but in its 27.3-day orbit around Earth, the Moon goes through day and night cycles like our planet. This is why we see it change in brightness from being full to a crescent; the Sun is shining on different parts of the Moon from our perspective, but there's no dark side — only a side that we cannot see.

"The Moon goes through day and night cycles"

CONSPIRACIES | TECH | SCIENCE | TRANSPORT | SPACE | ENVIRONMENT | HISTORY

There is a far side of the Moon (left), but there's no dark side

We unravel some common misconceptions about the natural world

Homo habilis ma...
used the first sto...

"HUMANS EVOLVED FROM CHIMPANZEES"

"Chimps and hu...
evolved along...
one another, r...
than us desce...
from them...

Although there are similarities between humans and chimpanzees, such as opposable thumbs and facial features, but chimps didn't just shed their fur and start making fires. We are, however, genetically related to chimps through our common ancestors, along with other great apes like gorillas and bonobos.

The first sign of primates on Earth dates back to around 55 million years ago (MYA). Then, from a common ancestor, chimps and humans split into two distinct genetic timelines between 8–6 MYA, although a more recent study suggests that divergence may have occurred up to 13 MYA. Our primate cousins continued to evolve into the apes we see today, whereas others evolved into the group known as Hominini, of which we are the only surviving species.

Chimpanzees remained in the group Hominoidea, which divides over 20 species between great apes such as orangutans and lesser apes such as gibbons.

It was around 5.8 MYA that one of our proposed ancestors — *Orrorin tugenensis* — walked on two legs, despite closely resembling a chimpanzee. About 4 MYA, our prehistoric species developed a brain more representative of the *Homo sapiens* we are today — these more advanced ancestors were *Australopithecus afarensis*. Our use of tools dates back some 2.6 MYA, regularly used by *Homo habilis* and *Homo erectus*, who around 1.8 MYA, was the first to stand up straight.

Though we started our evolutionary journey together, chimps and humans evolved alongside one another rather than us descending from them.

Strong bonds
Each carbon atom inside a diamond is covalently bonded to four other carbon atoms.

The word 'diamond' is derived from the Greek word 'adamas', meaning invincible or indestructible

Under pressure
Created under intense pressure and heat, diamonds are the hardest natural mineral.

"DIAMONDS ARE MADE FROM COAL"

It is often thought that diamonds form from the compression of coal, but these beautiful gems originate from a deeper geology. The confusion comes from their similarly high content of carbon. Both diamonds and coal are made of carbon, but they form in different layers within the Earth.

Diamonds form in the Earth's mantle, around 145 kilometres below the surface. At temperatures of around 1,050 degrees Celsius, diamonds form from carbon under the immense pressure of the Earth's mantle. Ejected via volcanic eruptions, diamonds are pushed to the surface, hitching a ride on a magma channel rising from the mantle.

Diamonds have also been known to come from the subduction zone, where an oceanic plate collides with a continental plate, forcing the oceanic plate underneath its continental counterpart. This process occurs at a lower temperature and pressure, so smaller diamonds are formed.

On the other hand, as a sedimentary rock, coal is the product of the decomposition of natural materials such as sea life and plant material. Coal is formed much higher up in the mantle, and is rarely buried to depths greater than 3.2 kilometres. Though it would make a great rags to riches story, in the case of diamonds, it's riches all the way.

Once cut and polished, diamonds present their unique sparkle

"CAMELS' HUMPS ARE FILLED WITH WATER"

In order to survive the intense heat of the desert climate, one or two giant biological water bottles sounds like a great idea. But the idea of a camels' hydrating humps are just a myth, but a myth not far from the truth. Rather than being filled with water, camels' humps are filled with fat.

Similar to the lack of water, deserts aren't known for their lush green vegetation. These mobile mounds of fat stores offer energy for camels to make use of when food is scarce. The longer the time between meals, the more deflated these humps appear as their resources are being used up. This isn't to say that camels don't consume a lot of water; they just don't store it in their humps. When arriving at a watery oasis, the two-humped Bactrian camel, for example, can drink over 100 litres of water in one go.

But, camels do have biological adaptations to optimise water storage. For example, camels' faeces is dry, they have little urine output and are able to fluctuate their body temperature to reduce levels of sweat. So, while their humps aren't filled with water, they have made the changes needed to survive in the harsh climate of the desert.

Bactrian camels (pictured) can be found in the Gobi Desert

"CLOUDS ARE LIGHTWEIGHT"

Like cotton wool, clouds are always used to describe the lighter things in life. But while they may glide gracefully around a blue sky, clouds are the heavyweight giants of our atmosphere. When you consider the amount of water that comes from a massive downpour, imagine how heavy the cloud must have been to hold it.

The water density of an average fluffy cumulus cloud is about 0.5 grams per cubic metre. If you propose a cloud that is one kilometre long, tall and wide, that gives you a total of 1 billion cubic metres in volume. That works out at around 500 tons of water — the same as around two and half blue whales floating above our heads! This method also suggests that larger and denser cumulonimbus clouds could weigh around 1 million tons! It's a huge weight, but the surrounding atmosphere is denser than the cloud, so it floats. Temperature also plays a part in keeping these clouds in the air, as warmer air is less dense than cool.

As we know, when a cloud gets too full of water, droplets form and we get rain, and the weight of the cloud reduces as a result. So next time it's a cloudy day and pouring it down, there could be literally tons of water falling over your head.

Bananas grow in what are known as 'hands'

"BANANAS ARE A FRUIT"

It's another 'is a tomato a fruit or a vegetable?' debate. Botanically, a fruit is defined as a seed-bearing structure that develops from the flowering plants of a woody tree or bush. The evolutionary purpose for this structure is to entice animals to eat the juicy sweet or sour fruit, helping to spread the seeds in their waste, thereby helping plants reproduce.

The humble banana, however, does not encapsulate its seeds around a fleshy fruit. Instead, the small black seeds (the little dots in the middle) are within the banana's flesh, making it more of a berry, which they would be classified as if their seeds were fertile. Since bananas have been commercially grown the seeds do not mature, and the 'tree' a banana grows on doesn't contain true woody tissue, making them a simple herb.

There are ten main groups of cloud that cross the sky

Goldfish are able to identify a familiar face among 44 strangers

"GOLDFISH HAVE THREE-SECOND MEMORIES"

'You've got the memory of a goldfish' is something often heard over your shoulder while you're hunting for a bundle of misplaced keys. This myth began when humans decided to take these orange iridescent fish as pets. Some think that the myth originated as a justification for keeping fish in small tanks. By the time they had done one lap of the bowl it would be a new experience going around the second, then the third time, and so on.

However, studies have shown this to be untrue. Research has revealed that goldfish can remember food locations and even the people who feed them. Just think, when you go to feed your goldfish, do they come up to greet you? One study by The Technion – Israel Institute of Technology conducted a fascinating study to test out this myth.

The research team trained captive fish to associate a particular sound with that of feeding time. They continued this for a month before releasing them into the wild. The fish were left in the wild for five months, the sound was then played again and the fish that remembered the association between the sound and food came back. So the next time you lose your keys, try asking the goldfish.

"LIGHTNING NEVER STRIKES IN THE SAME PLACE TWICE"

In the US there are around 30 fatalities due to lightning strikes each year

It's a common myth that if you stand where a lightning bolt just struck then you're safe. It appears that probability is the driving force behind this potentially dangerous myth, but there is a higher chance to be struck twice than you'd think.

In order for a lightning bolt to hit the ground, a discharge of pent up electrical energy within the cloud travels through ionised air. In a matter of milliseconds, the strike reverberates, meaning multiple strikes occur during what appears to be singular event. As this is a cloud-to-ground event, the closer objects on the Earth's surface are to the cloud, the more likely they are to be struck. Take the Empire State Building, for example, which gets hit an average of 23 times a year. Fortunately, it is equipped with lightning rods to help ground the charge in order to keep everyone inside safe.

1. A perfect storm
The movement of water and ice droplets within clouds can create charge separation. As rising droplets collide with falling ice or sleet particles, electrons can get knocked off of the rising moisture.

2. Charge separation
These collisions lead to the separation of charge within the cloud, with negatively charged ions at the base and the positively charged rising moisture at the top.

Multiple types
In order for lightning to be generated, positive and negative ions must be separated. It can occur as cloud-to-gound, cloud-to-cloud, cloud-to-air and intra-cloud.

4. Neutralise the charge
The opposing positive and negative charges seek to neutralise one another. When the difference in charge gets too high, the surrounding air becomes ionised (separated into electrons and positive ions), helping electrons to move more easily.

3. Repulsion
If the charge separation builds to a sufficient level, the negative charge of the cloud base becomes strong enough to repel negative electrons in the ground, inducing a positive charge on the surface below.

5. Lightning strikes
The ionised air creates a path between the cloud and the ground which electrons can travel through. This leads to a rapid discharge of electricity, which we see as lightning.

CONSPIRACIES TECH SCIENCE TRANSPORT SPACE ENVIRONMENT HISTORY

Armour grew progressively thicker in later centuries to protect against the threat of firearms

Not everything you've read about in the history books is entirely true...

"KNIGHTS HAD TO BE HOISTED ONTO THEIR HORSES"

Although they look incredibly heavy, 15th century suits of armour weigh in at around 14–23 kilograms. Despite this, they were not difficult to move about in or mount a horse while wearing. Knights had to remain as agile as possible in order to stay combat effective, or even just survive a melee. If armour really had been so heavy that a fallen knight could not have stood up again on his own, or been able to re-mount his horse, the smallest trip in battle would have been a death sentence.

While the metal plates had to be tough enough for ample protection, they also had to be light enough for prolonged action and a range of movement. A suit of plate armour could be comprised of around 18 main separate pieces, each protecting a different limb or vital organ. Importantly, each piece had to move flexibly with the wearer, and without restricting any movement such as a sword swing or even some light running.

One of the origins of the impossibly heavy armour is found in the 1944 film *Henry V*, produced by Laurence Olivier. This depicts knights being hoisted onto their mounts using cranes — a bizarre fiction with no historical evidence. By contrast, there are historical accounts of armoured soldiers performing almost acrobatic feats, including Bertrand du Guesclin, who is recorded leaping to and from his horse.

Modern-day soldiers, by comparison, regularly take more than 50 kilograms of armour, weaponry and equipment into combat, the majority of which is carried in their backpacks. With a suit of armour, the weight is spread mostly evenly over the wearer's entire body, making it much easier to bear and balance while wearing. This means that far from being restricted by impossibly heavy armour, knights fighting centuries ago were arguably more light and agile than their 21st-century counterparts.

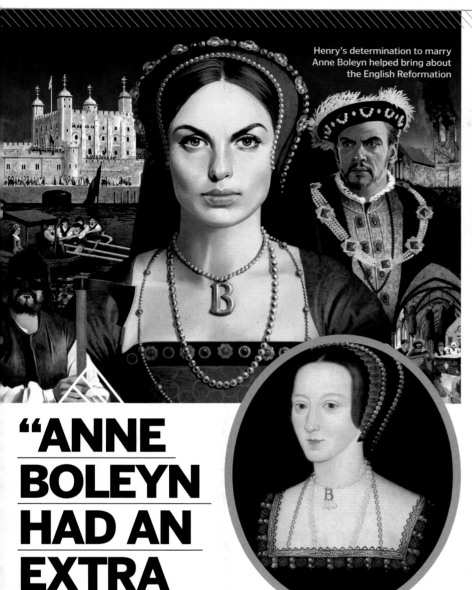

Henry's determination to marry Anne Boleyn helped bring about the English Reformation

Most paintings of the controversial queen were destroyed after her death

Vomitoriums were actually the entrances of amphitheatres

"ANNE BOLEYN HAD AN EXTRA FINGER"

Famous for being the doomed second wife of Henry VIII, Anne Boleyn was charged with adultery, incest and high treason. She had faced many accusations, but having an extra finger wasn't one of them. In fact, the claim wasn't even made during her lifetime.

Decades after Boleyn's death, a Catholic propagandist called Nicholas Sander wrote that she had "a projecting tooth under the upper lip, and on her right hand, six fingers". He added that she had a large wart under her chin. In Tudor England physical imperfections were thought to be a sign of evil, and Sander had portrayed Boleyn as a witch who had seduced the king. But would such an unsightly woman have captured the heart of the Tudor tyrant? It seems very unlikely, for so determined was Henry to marry her that he broke away from the

Catholic Church and established his own – the Church of England.

Nicholas Sander never actually met Boleyn in person and was only a boy when she was beheaded in 1536. It's likely Anne's rumoured disfigurements were a way of discrediting her daughter, Queen Elizabeth I. It was her religious policies that forced Sander into exile, and he wasn't alone in attacking the Protestant monarch's parentage in a vengeful bid to sully her name.

What's more, Anne's first biographer, George Wyatt, had spoken to those who knew her and admitted that while she did have several moles and an extra nail on her little finger, there was no sixth digit. And when a body believed to have been Boleyn was exhumed at the Tower of London in the 19th century, there was no evidence to support Sander's slander.

"VOMITORIUMS WERE USED FOR THROWING UP IN"

The Romans were fond of a feast. They would gorge on delicacies like wild boar, pheasant, lobsters and songbirds until they couldn't eat any more. That's when they would take a trip to the vomitorium – a room where the diner could expel their previous courses and return to eat some more. Or so pop culture would have us believe.

In ancient Rome, vomitoriums were actually the entrance and exit passages of amphitheatres. The 5th-century writer Macrobius chose this charming Latin word because of the way people 'spewed forth' into their seats at these open-air venues.

It seems people may have got confused over time, which isn't surprising given the infamous gluttony of Rome's emperors. Claudius was said to always finish a meal bloated and confined to bed, while Vitellius allegedly ate the sacrificial meat from an altar! But even emperors didn't have a special chunder chamber.

Marie Antoinette being led to her execution on 16 October 1793

"MARIE ANTOINETTE SAID 'LET THEM EAT CAKE'"

When the wife of King Louis XVI was told her French subjects had no bread to eat, she retorted, "Let them eat cake." Or did she? It was 1789, crop failures had left the starving population deeply resentful of the monarchy, and the Austrian-born queen became their target. However, the phrase 'let them eat cake' had been used for years. More than a century earlier, Marie-Thérèse – the Spanish bride of King Louis XIV – supposedly said the French people should eat "the crust of the pâté".

The infamous remark stuck though, and Marie Antoinette's reputation for decadence was blamed for causing the country's economic downturn. While it's true that she embraced life at Versailles, her love of palace parties, fashion and gambling wasn't the cause of the French Revolution. Nevertheless, the misunderstood monarch was sentenced to death along with the rest of the royal family, but the myth survived her.

CONSPIRACIES | TECH | SCIENCE | TRANSPORT | SPACE | ENVIRONMENT | HISTORY

This cartoon of Napoleon by artist James Gillray shows the 'little' emperor ranting and raving at the freedoms in England

"NAPOLEON WAS SHORT"

Despite conquering much of Europe single-handedly, Napoleon Bonaparte is almost as well known for his short stature. But, in reality the emperor of France was around five foot, 6.5 inches (1.69 metres) tall, making him above average height for men in both France and England at that time.

When he died in 1821, Napoleon was measured to be five foot, 2 inches (1.57 metres) tall. Unfortunately for the deceased, this was taken in French feet and inches, which were slightly larger than English measurements. In the early 19th century the metric system was not yet used universally, meaning there was no standarised measurement. When interpreted as English feet, Napoleon's height was therefore mistakenly recorded as being over four inches shorter.

However, even before his death the emperor had been mocked for his supposed tiny size. Another source of

this myth is found in the British press of the period. Newspaper columns roundly criticised Napoleon, printing caricatures depicting him as a tiny child throwing temper tantrums. This impression was aided by his nickname 'Le Petit Caporal' (the little corporal) among his troops, and the fact his personal bodyguard, the Old Guard, had a minimum height requirement of six feet (1.8 metres), towering above him by comparison.

This myth has proven so persuasive that a theoretical condition was named after the emperor's supposedly short stature. The 'Napoleon complex' suggests that shorter-than-average men become more aggressive, seek more attention in social gatherings and possess greater ambition than average-height or tall men. Experts still question the accuracy of this, but what's certain is that Napoleon was by no means vertically challenged.

"300 SPARTANS ALONE FOUGHT THE PERSIAN ARMY AT THERMOPYLAE"

In 480 BCE King Leonidas made a brave last stand against a horde of enemies at the head of only 300 of his ferocious hoplite warriors. It is one of the most compelling stories of ancient Greece, but is it entirely true?

In reality, between 6,000–7,000 fellow Greeks joined the Spartans at the Battle of Thermopylae, travelling from across Greece to defend against the Persian invasion led by King Xerxes I. Among those fighting with the 300 Spartans, Herodotus lists 700 Thespians, 400 Thebans, 1,120 Arcadians, 1,000 Phocians, and more. Nonetheless, the Greeks were still greatly outnumbered against up to 100,000 Persian soldiers.

The Greek army was deployed in a narrow coastal pass, nicknamed the Hot Gate, where the overwhelming numbers of attacking Persians could not be effected. According to Herodotus, the crucial turning point in the battle came when the Persian army was led to a secret mountain

pass, enabling them to overcome the Phocian guards.

In the 2006 film *300*, it is at this point that the Spartans' allies abandon them out of fear, while Leonidas declares he and his men will stay and fight to the death. However, even this scene is inaccurate, as several of the Greek allies remained fighting to the bitter end, including those forces from Thespiae and Thebes.

While the Thespians reportedly stayed willingly with Leonidas, Herodotus writes that the king kept the Theban troops against their will. Regardless, the Persian army eventually crushed their Greek opponents, who had fought their way into legend.

King Leonidas I died at Thermopylae along with his 300 Spartan hoplites and their allies

© Shutterstock; WIKI; Getty

Experts believe Vikings wore protective skullcaps made from metal or leather

Vikings were colonists who left their mark on many countries across Europe

CONSPIRACIES

TECH

SCIENCE

TRANSPORT

SPACE

ENVIRONMENT

HISTORY

"VIKINGS WORE HORNED HELMETS"

Vikings were seafaring Scandinavians that raided, traded and garnered a bloodthirsty reputation between the 8th to 11th centuries. The famous beastly horned helmets seem to fit the stereotype, but there's actually no evidence to suggest they ever wore them.

This myth was popularised after writers and artists used the headgear in their portrayals of Vikings. In the 1870s, German costume designer Carl Emil Doepler, created horned helmets for Wagner's Norse-inspired opera, and is often credited with cementing this stereotype. Perhaps these creators were inspired by

19th-century archaeological discoveries of horned helmets — but these were later found to predate the Vikings.

The only shred of evidence that can be called 'Viking' was discovered at a Gjermundbu burial mound, but this 10th-century artifact does not have any horns. It's possible such helmets were used for ceremonial purposes, but it's very unlikely they were worn aboard warships — the space would have been too limited — and they wouldn't be practical in battle either. Instead, it's thought that Norsemen wore leather skullcaps or domed metal helmets with brow

ridges, fragments of which have been discovered. It could also be possible that some Vikings didn't wear any headgear at all, which would explain why only a small number of helmets have been found.

That's not the only myth surrounding the Vikings though. Portrayed as beardy, illiterate savages, we've since discovered they groomed themselves with combs and razors; they developed a complex alphabet of runes; and while some spilled a lot of blood in their bid to conquer foreign lands, others earned a peaceful living through farming and trading.

TECHNOLOGY

040
Life in 2050

048
Real-time translators

049
Daisy: The iPhone eater

052
Epic engineering

"Amazing architecture and innovative designs that enable us to defy gravity"

058
Bulletproof glass

059
The first Robocop

ENHANCED REALITY

HYPERSONIC TRAVEL

MEDICAL IMPLANTS

LIFE IN 2050

WELCOME TO THE WORLD OF THE NEXT GENERATION

Words by **James Horton**

3D-PRINTED ORGANS

FULLY AUTOMATED DRIVING

ROBOTICS REVOLUTION

Tomorrow's cities will be home to vertical farms, enhanced greenery and a multitude of new buildings

Brain-computer interfaces will allow us to control tomorrow's technology by thought alone

Delivery services, provided by autonomous drones, will be faster and cheaper than today's options

S prawling, eco-friendly megacities, a global population exceeding 9.8 billion, and far-reaching inventions that marry biology and technology all lay ahead of us. Today's world is one filled with ideas, innovation and imagination, making us perfectly poised to speculate on what the world will become in just over three decades.

It may seem dangerous to cast our eyes so far ahead, across decades of exponential progress. But in today's research we find the seeds of the era-defining technologies that will come to be. In the 1950s, Alan Turing considered the 'ghost in the machine' and challenged his contemporaries to consider whether we could truly create intelligent – if not sentient – machines. Now, with deep neural networks and other artificial intelligence approaches we find ourselves edging ever closer to an idea first posed over 60 years ago. Turing's vision has almost been realised, and within this feature we will uncover analogous ideas that may grow, just as Turing's vision did, into technologies that will bring similar disruption to the world of 2050.

MAKING NEW STRIDES

As the collective pool of human knowledge continues to expand, we will increasingly see branches of research broaden their perspective and bleed into different areas of investigation. Such fusions of science and technology will play a pivotal role in the years to come. For example, forensics may start incorporating the staggeringly broad applicability of data science. Researchers at Oxford University have for the first time uncovered genetic variations that are strongly associated with particular facial features. As we move forward and others

> "In today's research we find the seeds of the era-defining technologies that will come to be"

inevitably expand on this novel finding – and the link between a person's unique genetic code and their facial features is revealed – a wanted person's DNA will suddenly reveal much more than just a simple match on a known criminal database. Amazingly, police officers in 2050 will likely be able to create an accurate facial model from a mere drop of saliva or a single strand of hair. Then, with the help of smart computer systems, they will be able to scour the area with drones and locate their target.

At the centre of these cross-disciplinary technological marvels, however, will lie brain-computer interfaces similar to the kind being developed by Elon Musk's Neuralink. This intriguing company endeavours to create a neural mesh capable of directly linking to the cloud, forming a bridge between our thoughts and the electronic world around us. Musk rightly points to our current reliance on smartphones – and namely how we loathe to be without them – as evidence that we're already bound to technology. But in 2050 this connection will have deepened to the extent that we will have access to implants that form a neural interface around the outside of our brains.

For those equipped with such technology, information from the web will be directly delivered to their thoughts on a moment's notice (much to the chagrin of pub quiz runners); electronic devices will be controlled just by thought; and people will be able to enjoy

> ### "Most meat will be lab grown rather than traditionally farmed"

'consensual telepathy'. This may seem the product of sorcery, but in 2050, when technology will be even more integral and abundant than it is today, interfaces that permit easier interactions with our creations will become hugely advantageous. The medical applications of this technology are also worthy of mention, as those with brain and other central nervous system injuries will be able to utilise this tech to circumvent severed connections via the cloud. As a result, communications between the brain and limb will be restored, and those who are severely paralysed will be able to more easily interact with the outside world.

The places we inhabit will also have transformed by 2050. For those who live in rural areas, more land will become available for biodiversity to prosper in once more as agricultural land will be stripped back. With a swelling population we may expect farming land demand to grow rather than dwindle, but many meats will be available in the form of lab-grown varieties, and cities will employ vertical farming to generate food supplies.

Off-world mining

Many nations throughout the world are committed to cutting down their carbon footprint in the coming decades, with the hope that by 2050 it will be significantly reduced. A vital part of this vision includes an increased reliance on batteries and other electronics, which will be key for renewable energies and emission-free electric cars. But mining enough precious metals to meet the ever-growing demand represents a serious hurdle.

One undesirable answer to this problem is to employ deep-sea mining that targets hydrothermal vents. These are known to be rich in metal deposits but are truly remarkable oases of life (and may even be where life began), so a better alternative is needed. This will come in the form of off-world mining on local asteroids as well as our closest companion – the Moon.

Mining the Moon holds great promise thanks to its deposits of helium-3, an isotope ejected from the Sun that will eventually be used as fuel in nuclear fusion reactors. With robot workers and giant 3D printers to create infrastructure, off-world mining will be able to provide us with a continuous supply of precious and much-needed resources.

Mining precious metals off-world will be integral for the future production of electronics

YOUR FUTURE LIFE

Fill the shoes of tomorrow's citizen and uncover what an average day will be like in 2050

19:30pm
To help reduce harmful emissions and intensive farming, most meat will be lab grown rather than traditionally farmed. This will vastly reduce waste as well as the need for large areas of pasture.

9:00am
Most labour and administrative jobs will be completed autonomously, which means many members of the adult population will receive Universal Income and enjoy complete freedom of their time.

17:30pm
Virtual reality headsets, haptic-feedback suits and blistering connection speeds will mean we'll be able to game inside immersive and expansive digital worlds.

9:30am
Advancements in AI and quantum computing will allow us to create truly powerful artificial brains, which will, in part, act as intelligent virtual assistants.

17:00pm
Hyperloop vehicles, housed in cylindrical tunnels underground and above our heads, will travel at nearly 1,000kph to get us home.

10:00am
Battery-powered, self-driving cars will be readily available as an affordable, safe and eco-friendly taxi service whenever we need it.

15:00pm
Adverts will interact with our augmented reality headsets to create 3D holograms featuring carefully selected products.

11:45am
Increased global trade will lead to a cryptocurrency taking the lead as a universal digital currency to pay for whatever, wherever we are.

14:30pm
Thanks to Universal Income there will be ample opportunity to book a holiday. Upgrade your ticket to a hypersonic flight and you'll be able to reach anywhere on Earth in just a few hours.

12:00pm
Travelling to meetings will be unnecessary thanks to high-definition augmented reality headsets, which will enable interaction in 3D space.

Vertical farming, where tiers of crops are stacked atop one another, may take up residence as great glass skyscrapers in tomorrow's cities. There, they will be able to grow nutritious crops including tomatoes, lettuces and greens, as well providing greenery to the urban landscape. Smaller-scale vertical farms may also be affixed to the sides of older buildings, providing cleaner air and extra food sources. It has been estimated that the largest vertical farm structures could provide food for up to 50,000 people. Food loss from transport and storage will be eradicated, fewer pesticides would be needed thanks to the segregated environments, and crops could be grown throughout the year. And, as an added bonus, sealed vertical farms would naturally recycle their own water supply, making the process even more economical.

As a whole, we will find 2050's megacities considerably better equipped and more self-sufficient than those of today. Bioengineered microorganisms will help to clean the water supply, lowering the energy expenditure required for water processing, and we may even save power in the evenings as street lights are replaced by glowing trees. These will be products of technologies that will build upon the success of MIT scientists, who at the end of 2017 successfully engineered leaves using nanoparticles that glowed vibrantly under the plant's own power. Providing both light and beauty to the city, the glowing trees will help transform our metropolises from concrete jungles into otherworldly visual spectacles.

THE RISE OF AUTOMATION

Some of the ideas we have visited thus far in this feature have been likely, some a little more speculative and others wishful, but one thing that companies the world over are barrelling toward is autonomous systems. A world dominated by self-acting machines seems to be

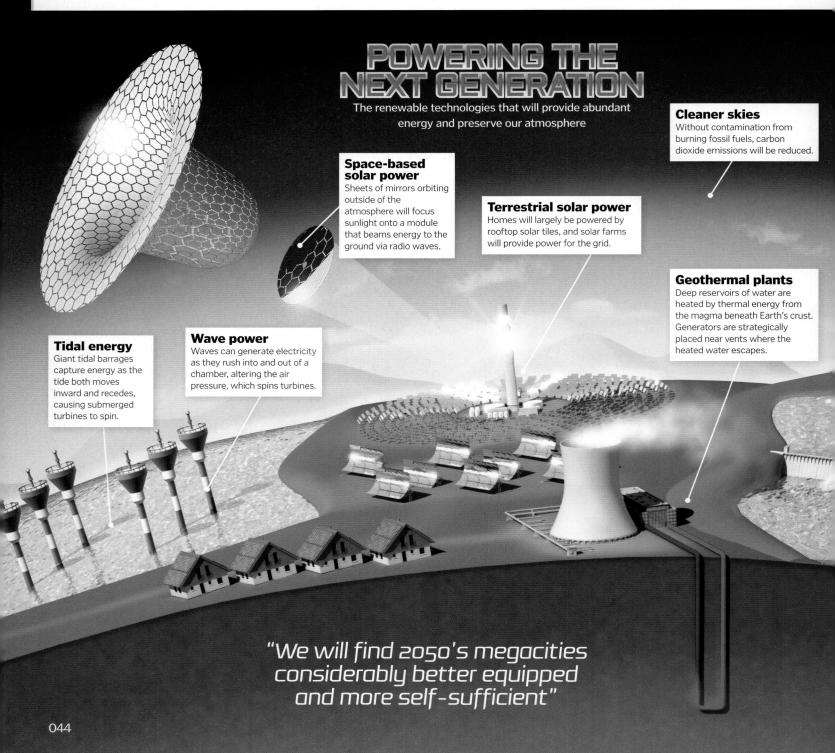

POWERING THE NEXT GENERATION

The renewable technologies that will provide abundant energy and preserve our atmosphere

Cleaner skies
Without contamination from burning fossil fuels, carbon dioxide emissions will be reduced.

Space-based solar power
Sheets of mirrors orbiting outside of the atmosphere will focus sunlight onto a module that beams energy to the ground via radio waves.

Terrestrial solar power
Homes will largely be powered by rooftop solar tiles, and solar farms will provide power for the grid.

Geothermal plants
Deep reservoirs of water are heated by thermal energy from the magma beneath Earth's crust. Generators are strategically placed near vents where the heated water escapes.

Tidal energy
Giant tidal barrages capture energy as the tide both moves inward and recedes, causing submerged turbines to spin.

Wave power
Waves can generate electricity as they rush into and out of a chamber, altering the air pressure, which spins turbines.

"We will find 2050's megacities considerably better equipped and more self-sufficient"

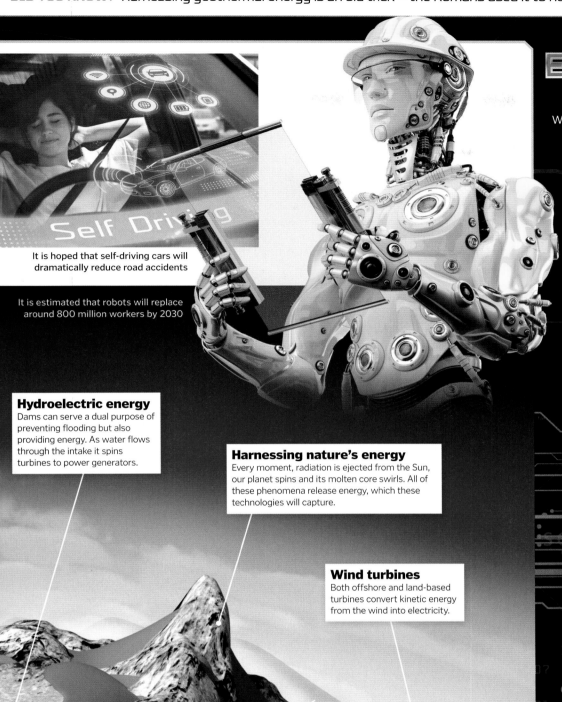

Self Driving

It is hoped that self-driving cars will dramatically reduce road accidents

It is estimated that robots will replace around 800 million workers by 2030

Hydroelectric energy
Dams can serve a dual purpose of preventing flooding but also providing energy. As water flows through the intake it spins turbines to power generators.

Harnessing nature's energy
Every moment, radiation is ejected from the Sun, our planet spins and its molten core swirls. All of these phenomena release energy, which these technologies will capture.

Wind turbines
Both offshore and land-based turbines convert kinetic energy from the wind into electricity.

ECO-FRIENDLY IN 2050
Welcome to a future built on renewable and sustainable energy sources

139
The number of countries that could be powered entirely by renewable energies in 2050

24 million
The net gain of jobs created for countries relying solely on renewable energy

2040
The year the UK plans to ban sales of vehicles powered by fossil fuels

42.5%
The estimated decrease in energy demand after we switch to efficient renewables

1.1 million tons
The estimated mass of helium-3 on the Moon's surface

48%
The predicted contribution of solar-power-based technologies to energy production in 2050

© Getty Illustration by Adrian Mann

etched into our destiny, as every year we uncover greater possibilities and achieve new milestones, some of which have come a decade before their predicted time.

Fortunately, this won't lead to an ominous revolution of robots and their artificial intelligences, but rather an integration of autonomous systems into nearly every facet of our lives. They will become the tireless worker drones that gather, process and organise our data, clean our offices, deliver our parcels and so much more. If we look around us today we can see that this change has already begun. Stock brokers rely on algorithms to predict fluctuations in the stock market; Facebook programs dig through our internet cookies to learn the right advertisements to feed us; and fast food chains are replacing staff with burger-flipping robots.

There are a slew of reasons for this major cultural shift. Algorithms and robots will prove cheaper for companies, more efficient, and when handling data, simply far superior than any human counterpart. The only major hurdle left to overcome in the following years involves teaching machines how to perform a job optimally. But once they've learnt it, you can be certain that they'll be much more capable than their human predecessors.

So what does this mean for jobs? For some, it'll mean a much easier working life. Such beneficiaries will of course include most large business owners, but disciplines such as medicine - and the patients that they treat - will be bolstered by artificially intelligent support. A multitude of disease diagnoses, for instance, are still assessed by eye alone. This outdated approach has an element of subjectivity and is prone to error, but machines that have been trained on tens of thousands of images will be able to aid medical practitioners by accurately diagnosing diseased tissue.

Yet for many others careers, machinated workers will simply offer a favourable alternative to human employees. One study estimated that certain sectors could see up to 50 per cent of jobs being handed over to robots and AI by 2030, and we can be certain that the following two decades will see machines grow exponentially more capable, and many other careers will come under threat. Jobs that require empathy and creativity are currently believed to be immune to the incoming influx of automation, but can we be so confident that a machine won't be able to outperform a human in these areas by 2050?

Those vying for the remaining jobs, which will likely include policing, governing, teaching, researching and counselling, will face a fiercely competitive environment, especially as the global population is set to increase to nearly 10 billion by 2050. As a result, we may find ourselves in the era of Universal Income, where the governments of the world will provide pay to adults without them having to work. This way the economy keeps turning and the population becomes able to invest their time in whatever they please, free from the pressure of generating income. It would represent the greatest change in our daily lives for hundreds of years and pave the way for people to continue the phenomenal technological upward trend of the past 50 years.

Tunnels kept at near-vacuum pressures will house superfast vehicles known as hyperloops, which will transport future citizens around at 1000kph

Extended lifespans

An ageing population can be a fearful prospect for future generations due to the economic pressures of having to provide and care for a considerable portion of a country's citizens. But what if old didn't have to mean infirm; what if we could prevent the effects of ageing and keep people fitter and healthier for longer? A reality such as this one should be in effect by 2050 with the help of revolutionary regenerative technologies such as telomere extension.

Telomeres are essentially the 'caps' on the ends of our chromosomes, made up of long strings of basic genetic building blocks that are slightly shortened every time a cell divides. When the telomere is gone the cell can no longer properly replicate, and instead it dies. In a way, telomeres represent our natural lifespans, and with recent progress researchers have shown that extending telomeres with the help of proteins can restore cell division and prolong life. So for someone born in 2050, age-related issues including hair loss, compromised bone marrow and heightened cancer susceptibility will be a problem from another century.

Enzymes that sustain telomeres may offset many age-related diseases

Robot workers will free future populations from many manual tasks, including those in agriculture

TOMORROW'S MEDICAL MILESTONES

Discover the top innovations that will transform the future of healthcare

Monitoring your health 24/7

Through wearable gadgets and small implants, key health indicators such as blood pressure, heart rate, cholesterol levels and blood sugar will all be recorded and transmitted continuously, ensuring that help will be at hand as soon as you need it.

3D printed organs

With basic biological components as the building material, bioprinters will be able to create new organs from the bottom-up. Simpler organs such as skin, and even more complex systems such as livers and lungs, will free patients from relying on donors.

The AI doctor

After decades of training intelligent algorithms to recognise patterns and symptoms of disease, 2050's 'consultant computers' will be able to reliably and accurately diagnose almost any condition and recommend the best course of treatment.

Synthetic blood cells

Plastic 'smart particles' that can bolster the immune response by binding to invading cells, and carbon-based 'respirocytes' carrying 100 times more oxygen than red blood cells, means future generations will enjoy near-superhuman levels of defence and fitness.

"For someone born in 2050, age-related issues will be a problem from another century"

Advanced bionics

The future of exoskeletons and artificial limbs will rely upon improved robotics for increased synthetic limb acuity, as well as brain-bionic interfaces that wirelessly transmit electrical signals from the brain to an attached appendage, meaning it can be moved by thought alone.

Speaking a different language
How does real-time translator technology work?

2 Transmitted
The received dialogue is transmitted via Bluetooth from the earbud to the user's smartphone.

1 "Hello"
Words spoken in one language are received by the microphone in the listener's earbud.

4 "Bonjour"
The spoken translation is transmitted back to the earbud and played back to the listener in their native language.

3 Translate
The speech is quickly translated into the desired language by the smartphone app's software.

The MARS earbuds won the Best of Innovation award at 2018's CES

Real-time translators

Could new technologies help us break down language barriers?

Unveiled at CES 2018, the MARS wireless earbuds (developed in a joint effort by the NAVER Corporation and LINE Corporation) showcased the future of real-time language translation. Powered by Clova AI, the MARS wireless Bluetooth earbuds can translate speech from another language into the wearer's native tongue almost instantly.

Clova works as a voice-controlled virtual assistant – similar to Alexa or Siri – that listens to your conversation and transmits the data to your smartphone via Bluetooth. The accompanying app then translates the speech and transmits a recording of the translation back to the earbuds, which play it back for you to hear. All this happens within a fraction of a second, so the translations are relayed in almost real time. Each pair of earbuds can work as a single translator for two people. For use in crowded areas, MARS also features noise-blocking technology to focus on individual conversations. The current MARS can translate between ten different languages, including English, Japanese and French, but 40 languages may be supported in the near future.

MARS isn't the only product breaking the language barrier. Waverly Labs have created The Pilot, which works in a similar fashion to the MARS. However, translations are consecutive, so you have to wait for a person to stop talking before the translation is then played back through the earbuds.

Google has put its eponymous Translate technology to use in their Google Pixel Buds. However, in this system only one person wears the earbuds. Their side of the conversation is translated and then played to the non-wearer via the app instead.

The Pilot earbuds have noise-blocking capabilities to minimise surrounding sounds

Daisy: The iPhone eater

Meet the machine that rips up iPhones for recycling

You might be surprised to learn that Apple has a machine designed specifically to tear iPhones apart, but it's true. At Apple's factory in Austin, Texas, and the company's European distribution centre, you'll find a robot called Daisy.

At first glance, Daisy looks like a machine that would put together an iPhone on the assembly line. Instead, it sorts through nine different iPhone models and separates all of their valuable parts for recycling. It's all automated, and Daisy can strip 200 iPhones in just an hour.

Based on years of research and design, Daisy removes and sorts useful components so that Apple can recover materials that normal recycling practices leave behind.

Typically, electronic devices are 'shredded', which can contaminate each metal and mean more smelting, refining and other expensive (and polluting) processes have to be completed. With Daisy, Apple can remove the most valuable components quickly and without damaging them so they can be melted down and used again more easily.

This is particularly important for recovering the rare earth magnets that drive the iPhone's speaker system. If an iPhone is shredded, these neodymium, praseodymium and dysprosium magnets cling to other metals and have to be discarded in the refining process.

All of this is particularly important because mining these materials – as well as tin and cobalt that are used in the solder and batteries respectively – is incredibly damaging to the environment. Mining produces huge amounts of carbon dioxide, so the more of these materials that can be recovered from old devices, the less environmental impact each new iPhone has.

The ultimate goal is to create a 'closed-loop' system, where new iPhones are made entirely from the recycled materials of old devices. With Daisy's help, Apple are a step closer to their goal.

Making the trip through Daisy
How Daisy recovers the precious materials inside your old iPhone

Hopper
A hopper pulls the iPhones out of a bin and puts them onto a conveyor belt, where a robotic arm grabs each one.

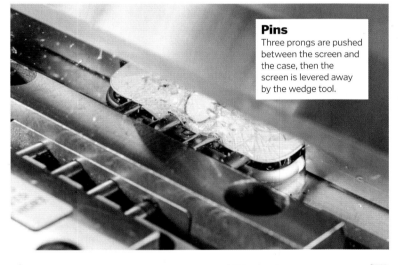

Pins
Three prongs are pushed between the screen and the case, then the screen is levered away by the wedge tool.

Wedge tool
Daisy peels the screen away from the rest of the casing with a wedge device. Its predecessor, Liam, used suction which didn't work well on damaged screens.

Component removal
A punching machine pushes screws out of the iPhone, then a pre-programmed auger removes the main components, like the camera, speaker and logic board.

Inside the Samsung Galaxy S9+

We take a look at what's happening inside Samsung's latest smartphone

The race for smartphone supremacy never stops, with the leading companies releasing new models every year to try and bring amazing new features to their customers. Samsung's latest offering brings a variable aperture lens to its camera system, something normally reserved for larger, dedicated cameras. The trick is that Samsung has included two tiny rotating discs into its camera that can open and close the aperture to allow more light into the lens. That means that you can get better low-light photos and still use the same camera to take everyday photos on sunny days. In fact, at f/1.5, the Galaxy S9+ has the widest aperture of any phone, so it's currently the market leader.

However, that's not the end of the innovation. The new biometric scanning cameras that face you when you pick up the phone can now be used to turn your face into an emoji! It's as simple as looking at the screen and letting the phone analyse your features. Soon, a cartoon version of yourself will appear in front of your eyes, meaning you can send personalised reactions to your friends. There's also a slow-mo camera that lets you record video and reduce the speed; auto-translate software that can show you live translations of words in the world around you; and a quick unlock system that uses your face and eyes as a password. It's a lot of tech for one small phone (especially when it's got such a big display), so let's find out how it all fits in there.

Thanks to the wider aperture lens you can get better shots even in low light

We lift the lid on the Galaxy S9+

How Samsung has packed so much advanced tech into such a small space

Colour range
The Galaxy S9+ is available in four main colours: Midnight Black, Lilac Purple, Coral Blue and Titanium Grey.

Fingerprint scanner
This small fingerprint scanner sits on the back of the phone just below the two cameras for another security option.

Dual camera
There are two rear cameras on the S9+. The first is the smart dual aperture camera, while the other lets you take lovely portrait photos.

Selfie camera
This front-facing eight-megapixel camera points at your face so you can take selfies. Smile!

Iris camera
The iris camera scans your eyes then combines this information with a facial scan to confirm your identity before unlocking the phone.

"The new biometric scanning cameras can turn your face into an emoji"

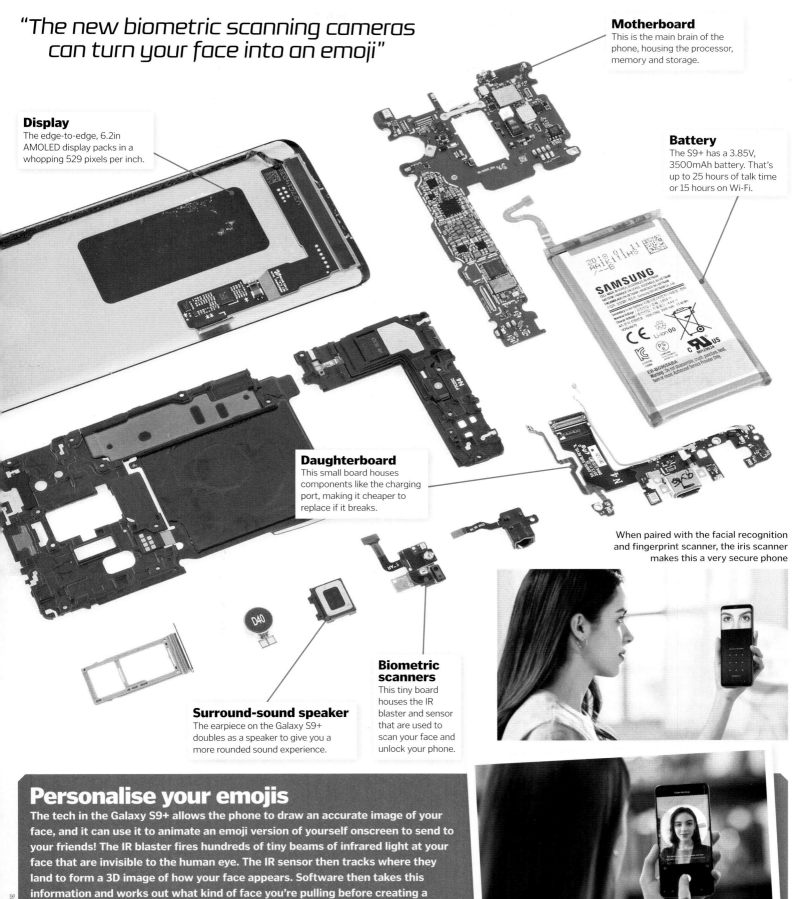

Motherboard
This is the main brain of the phone, housing the processor, memory and storage.

Display
The edge-to-edge, 6.2in AMOLED display packs in a whopping 529 pixels per inch.

Battery
The S9+ has a 3.85V, 3500mAh battery. That's up to 25 hours of talk time or 15 hours on Wi-Fi.

Daughterboard
This small board houses components like the charging port, making it cheaper to replace if it breaks.

When paired with the facial recognition and fingerprint scanner, the iris scanner makes this a very secure phone

Biometric scanners
This tiny board houses the IR blaster and sensor that are used to scan your face and unlock your phone.

Surround-sound speaker
The earpiece on the Galaxy S9+ doubles as a speaker to give you a more rounded sound experience.

Personalise your emojis

The tech in the Galaxy S9+ allows the phone to draw an accurate image of your face, and it can use it to animate an emoji version of yourself onscreen to send to your friends! The IR blaster fires hundreds of tiny beams of infrared light at your face that are invisible to the human eye. The IR sensor then tracks where they land to form a 3D image of how your face appears. Software then takes this information and works out what kind of face you're pulling before creating a similar expression on your animated avatar. It sounds complex, but the basic idea is that if you smile, your emoji will do the same in front of your eyes. It's that easy!

EPIC ENGIN

Behold incredible creations from the world's master builders. With innovations across the ocean, on land and deep underground, the sky is no longer the limit

Words by **James Horton**

SOARING STRUCTURES
Amazing architecture and innovative designs that enable us to defy gravity

W350 wooden skyscraper

■ **Location:** Tokyo, Japan
■ **Progress:** Planning stages, completion target 2041

The timber-framed tower designed to change cities into forests

Tall wooden buildings are growing both in popularity and in scale. At 53 metres in height, a student residence in Vancouver currently holds the title of the world's highest timber-framed building, but Tokyo may soon boast one nearly seven-times taller. Japanese company Sumitomo Forestry Co have proposed a 350-metre-tall wooden skyscraper to celebrate their 350th anniversary, which if commissioned will become Japan's tallest building.

With a predicted cost of just over £4 billion ($5.3 billion) – approximately double that of a traditional concrete skyscraper – the W350 would represent a big step towards Tokyo becoming a more environmentally friendly city. The organic aesthetic of the wooden structure will be bolstered by balconies on all four sides of the building, which will house an array of plant life.

To ensure the building remains stable – even in Tokyo, where seismic activity is common – it will be constructed using a 'braced tube structure'. This will involve a mixture of steel and wooden supports, with wood forming 90 per cent of the building's material.

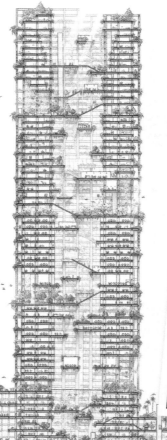

The W350 will house shops, offices, residential units and a hotel

The W350 will promote urban biodiversity by embedding flora on all of its many balconies

EERING

Beijing Daxing International Airport

■ **Location:** Beijing, China
■ **Progress:** Under construction, completion target 2019

China's latest infrastructure project will cater for 100 million passengers every year

Despite its size, the People's Republic of China has a relatively low aviation capacity. The Beijing Daxing International Airport was proposed to improve this, and it's set to do so in a big way.

This gargantuan airport, designed in collaboration with Zaha Hadid Architects, will feature four runways at the time of its opening and an intricate, flower-inspired terminal space built using 1.6 million cubic metres of concrete and 52,000 tons of steel. In total, the new airport will encompass an area of 47 square kilometres, and it has rightly been described as a testament to China's world-leading production capabilities.

Initially, Beijing's new airport is predicted to transport 45 million passengers per year, but this figure is expected to grow to a whopping 100 million passengers, making it one of the busiest airports in the world.

By 2025 it is hoped that the airport will be able to accommodate 630,000 flights a year

When it opens in late 2019, the Beijing Daxing will be the world's largest international airport

© Getty; Sumitomo Forestry & Nikken Sekkei; Render by Methanoia © Zaha Hadid Architects

GOING UNDERGROUND

With advanced tunnelling technologies, these projects are changing the infrastructure beneath our feet

Crossrail

■ **Location:** London, UK
■ **Progress:** Under construction, opens fully December 2019

The tunnels that represent the pinnacle of precision engineering

The Crossrail network was an ambitious undertaking, requiring eight tunnel boring machines to work 24 hours a day, seven days a week for three years. During that time the machines carved tunnels totalling 42 kilometres in length, but distance wasn't the only obstacle the Crossrail engineering team faced. To save on time and expenditure, the new tunnels ran as close as possible to their optimal path underneath London and came precariously close to existing infrastructure.

The machines had to avoid building foundations, sewers, utility tunnels and existing underground rail lines. Under the densely occupied underground of Tottenham Court Road, for example, the new tunnel came within one metre of an operational tube platform. Over 200,000 concrete segments were used to assemble the tunnel walls, and this structure was supplemented in places by additional sprayed concrete, which was used to reinforce the cross-passages that served to connect parallel rail lines.

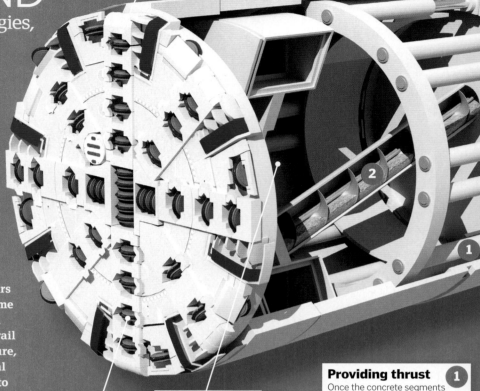

Laser guidance
The machines are governed by a laser guidance system, which ensures the tunnel ends up within 1mm of its target destination.

Stabilising pressure
To prevent the tunnel face collapsing, dirt removed by the cutting wheel is collected behind its face to provide stability.

Cutting wheel
The front face of the machine slowly revolves and carves away dirt using disc cutters and scraping tools.

Providing thrust ①
Once the concrete segments have formed a stable wall, pistons are pushed against them to drive the cutting wheel forwards.

The Boring Company

■ **Location:** Los Angeles, US
■ **Progress:** Trials ongoing

The tunnel company with an incredibly ambitious goal – to beat a snail in a race

Tunnel boring machines are slow – so slow, in fact, that a soft-soil variant is 14-times slower than a snail. But the Boring Company's founder, Elon Musk, has laid down the gauntlet: he wants his machine to beat a snail in a race.

Designing a carving machine that digs over 14-times faster than a traditional one is no mean feat, but Musk has a few ideas as to how this can be done. Most importantly, by placing vehicles inside the tunnel on an automated electric skate network, the tunnel's dimensions can be reduced substantially. This paves the way for an automated shuttle system that's set to revolutionise city travel, and it could be coming soon.

Inside the Boring Loop network

1 Departure
Private vehicles – along with public transport vehicles carrying between eight to 16 passengers – would enter the tunnel network at designated entry points.

Material analysis
Dirt being carried away on the conveyor belt is analysed to ensure the correct type of cutting wheel is being used.

Tunnel boring machines

The giant mechanical worms that create perfect tunnels and never need to rest

Crossrail's TBMs carved out approximately 3.4 million tons of earth over three years

Dirt removal **2**
Clay, chalk, soil and other geological materials are carried away from the cutting face via a revolving screw mechanism.

Lock and key **3**
Reinforced concrete segments are lifted into place via a mechanical arm. A conical-shaped keystone is added last to lock the segments in place.

Emisor Oriente water tunnel

■ **Location:** Mexico City, Mexico
■ **Progress:** Under construction, completion target 2018

The buried structure built to preserve Mexico City

Sewers aren't typically seen as the most glamorous of constructions, but the Emisor Oriente wastewater tunnel will soon be performing an invaluable service for Mexico City.

The city's growing population has led to an increased demand for water, which is pumped from the lakebed that lies beneath it. However, this has resulted in the city filling the void where the water used to be. Mexico's capital is sinking – possibly by as much as 12 metres in the past 100 years – and is now vulnerable to flooding.

Fortunately, engineering innovation is on hand to help. The Emisor Oriente will shift rainfall and wastewater at a rate of 150 cubic metres per second through its 62-kilometre length. Carved using six custom-built boring machines equipped to deal with the complex ground conditions in Mexico, the tunnel will be robust for years to come thanks to its wall of reinforced steel and concrete segmental rings.

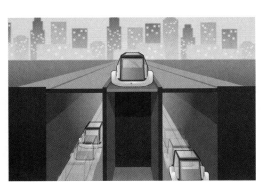

2 Descending
The entry points would operate as automated vertical lifts, which would safely descend from the surface into the tunnels below. From here the vehicles would merge into the relevant lane.

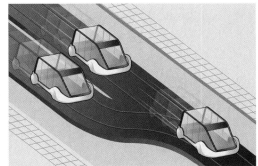

3 Gliding
Rather than driving independently within the tunnels, vehicles will be carried on a Loop system, an electric skate network that will ferry vehicles to their destinations at 200–240kph.

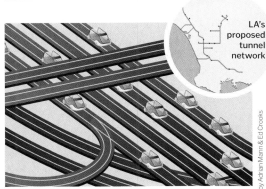

LA's proposed tunnel network

4 Future plans
There are plans for a 4.3km tunnel to be excavated in LA as a proof-of-process, but The Boring Company have also proposed a network of possible expansion routes across the city.

OVER WATER

How engineers harness the power of rivers and span huge natural barriers

Three Gorges Dam

■ **Location:** Sandouping, China
■ **Progress:** Completed, fully operational as of 2012

Meet the hydroelectric juggernaut that divides China's Yangtze River

The Three Gorges Dam is a monster. Its 2.3-kilometre length, 115-metre base width and maximum height of 185 metres spans the Yangtze River, making it the largest hydroelectric power station in the world.

By incorporating 27.2 million cubic metres of concrete and more than 460,000 metric tons of steel into its design, the dam supports an enormous reservoir that is capable of holding up to 42 billion tons of water.

Suffice to say, this dam can put out a lot of power. Estimated to generate 22,500 megawatts at maximum capacity, or around 11 times the energy output of the Hoover Dam in the US, the Three Gorges Dam has been pivotal to China shifting away from its reliance on fossil fuels and towards sources of renewable energy.

As well as generating energy, the dam was designed to alleviate flooding of the Yangtze Basin

The bridge is built to withstand earthquakes, super typhoons and being struck by a cargo vessel

Hong Kong-Zhuhai-Macau Bridge

■ **Location:** Lingdingyang Channel, China
■ **Progress:** Complete, opening 2018

The human-made thread of immense scale being built to connect three of China's most integral cities

The cities of Hong Kong and Zhuhai and the region of Macau have long been hindered in their interactions thanks to the Pearl River Estuary that separates them. But the three look set to become tied together in 2018 thanks to a land bridge that

The Three Gorges Dam cost $37 billion (approximately £28 billion) to build

The bridge's construction could even be seen in satellite imagery, pictured here by Landsat 8 in 2015

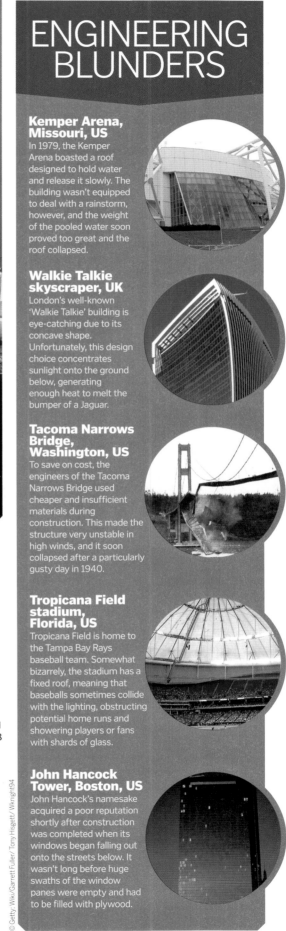

ENGINEERING BLUNDERS

Kemper Arena, Missouri, US
In 1979, the Kemper Arena boasted a roof designed to hold water and release it slowly. The building wasn't equipped to deal with a rainstorm, however, and the weight of the pooled water soon proved too great and the roof collapsed.

Walkie Talkie skyscraper, UK
London's well-known 'Walkie Talkie' building is eye-catching due to its concave shape. Unfortunately, this design choice concentrates sunlight onto the ground below, generating enough heat to melt the bumper of a Jaguar.

Tacoma Narrows Bridge, Washington, US
To save on cost, the engineers of the Tacoma Narrows Bridge used cheaper and insufficient materials during construction. This made the structure very unstable in high winds, and it soon collapsed after a particularly gusty day in 1940.

Tropicana Field stadium, Florida, US
Tropicana Field is home to the Tampa Bay Rays baseball team. Somewhat bizarrely, the stadium has a fixed roof, meaning that baseballs sometimes collide with the lighting, obstructing potential home runs and showering players or fans with shards of glass.

John Hancock Tower, Boston, US
John Hancock's namesake acquired a poor reputation shortly after construction was completed when its windows began falling out onto the streets below. It wasn't long before huge swaths of the window panes were empty and had to be filled with plywood.

will span around 55 kilometres – 20-times longer than the famous Golden Gate Bridge.

A considerable portion of the bridge – almost 30 kilometres of it – will straddle the estuary, and vehicles will travel over the water in three lanes on both sides. Artificial islands will then connect the bridge section to a 6.9-kilometre underwater tunnel, which will be submerged to allow ships to traverse the water. Official projections believe the bridge will reduce travel times between the cities from four hours to just 30 minutes, and what a sight people will behold as they travel.

"The bridge will lower travel times from four hours to just 30 minutes"

Bulletproof glass

How layers of plastic make this glass resistant to bullets

In the early 20th century, French chemist Édouard Bénédictus sandwiched celluloid between sheets of glass to create an early form of laminated safety glass. Bulletproof glass is based on an extension of the same principle: using multiple layers of glass and plastic to absorb the impact of bullets.

These protective panes are typically made with a plastic called polyvinyl butyral (PVB). Sheets of PVB, just a few millimetres thick, are sandwiched between each layer of glass. The layers are heated to melt the plastic layers so that they bond to the glass and strengthen it. Some panes may be as much as ten centimetres thick, but the number of layers used will vary depending on the glass' intended purpose.

Normal glass shatters on impact as it is unable to bend in order to absorb a bullet's energy, so the ammo continues hurtling along the line of fire without much loss of momentum. But if you have seen a cartoon where bullets are being fired at an indestructible piece of glass and bullets are bouncing back – that's not how it works. The bullets will still fracture the glass and pass into it, but as each layer of glass shatters it remains held together by the plastic. The kinetic energy of the bullet is spread out across the layers and quickly absorbed, stopping the shot in its tracks.

Normal glass can't slow a bullet as it is too brittle

Shatterproof science

How the energy-absorbing abilities of bulletproof glass can stop a speeding bullet

No bulletproof glass is technically 'bulletproof' – successive impacts will weaken the structure. Strictly speaking they are bullet resistant

Multiple layers
As energy is dissipated through the layers, the bullet is brought to a stop before it can exit the final sheet of glass.

Plastic
The soft, flexible polycarbonate layer bends, absorbing some of the bullet's kinetic energy and slowing it down.

Bullet
The bullet's kinetic energy dissipates quickly as it is transferred to the plastic layers, spreading out sideways over a large area.

Glass
The bullet shatters the glass that is held together by the plastic layer.

© Getty; Pixabay; Science Photo Library

The robocop is used as a tool for the Dubai police, rather than a replacement for officers

The first Robocop

Patrolling the streets of Dubai, meet the first automated police officer of the Middle East

Autonomous machines and robots are being introduced into the workforce of many industries, from manufacturing to retail. Moving with this trend, the Dubai Government introduced its first humanoid robot into their police ranks last year. Designed and built by PAL Robotics and programmed by the Dubai police, this fully autonomous humanoid is able to assist the public in cases of emergency and general enquiry.

Beneath its official uniform is the REEM robot, which has integrated AI enabling it to patrol through busy areas such as shopping centres and communicate with the public. Equipped with facial-recognition software and a live camera feed, REEM can keep an eye out for anyone of interest to the police, or investigate suspicious packages. Its software can detect the faces of wanted criminals or number plates of cars by automatically comparing images to those in a police database.

REEM has an iPad-style interface embedded in its chest for the public to report crimes on or hit the SOS button for immediate help 24 hours a day. Though it's hard to imagine REEM tackling any wrong-doers, the Dubai Government has faith that this style of 'robocop' could account for 25 per cent of the country's police force by 2030.

Speech
REEM is able to speak nine languages and understands voice commands in English and Russian.

Interface
A touchscreen chest allows the public to choose from several options to report a range of crimes.

Sight
Law enforcement officials can access the live camera feed from lenses in REEM's eyes.

Size
Built on a human scale, REEM is 1.7m tall and weighs 100kg.

Power
Robocop can stay on duty for eight hours before needing to be recharged.

Movement
Autonomous navigation allows REEM to avoid obstacles and even manoeuvre through crowds.

Hard exterior
The REEM robot is made from long-lasting material, protecting it from damage.

© Getty; PAL Robotics

059

SCIENCE

062
Are we still evolving?

080
Food waste

069
How do we sense time?

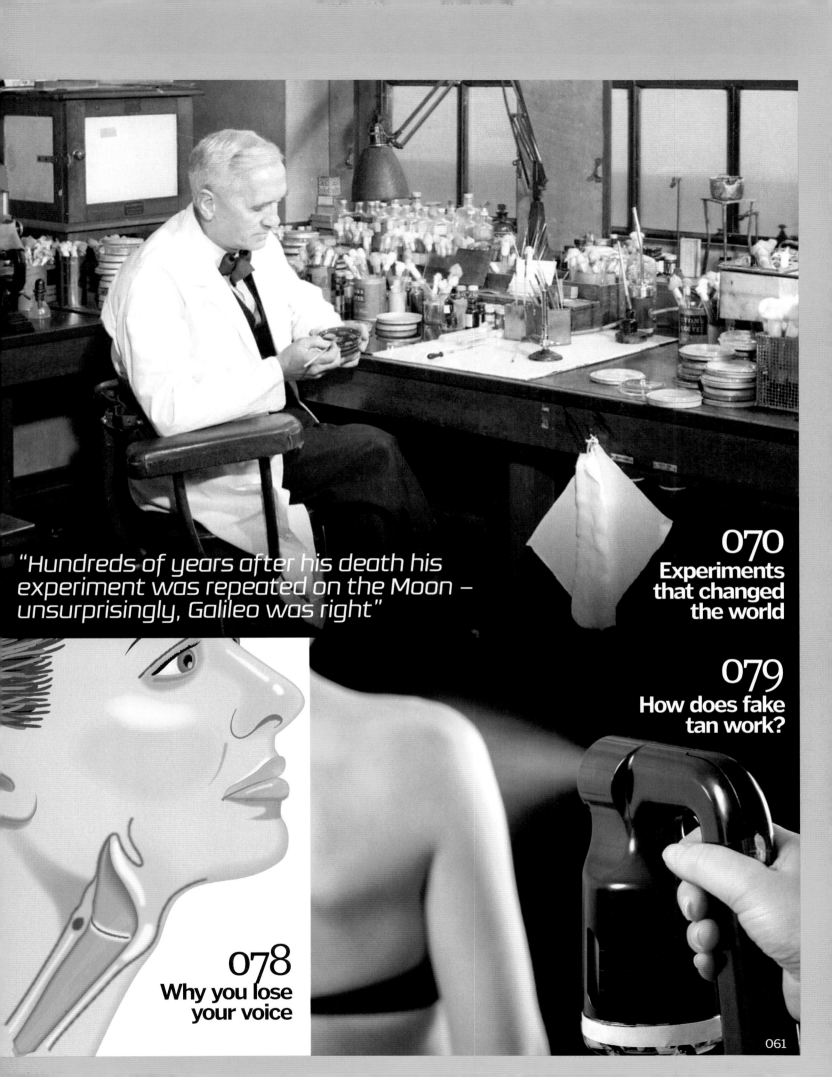

"Hundreds of years after his death his experiment was repeated on the Moon – unsurprisingly, Galileo was right"

070
Experiments that changed the world

079
How does fake tan work?

078
Why you lose your voice

061

ARE WE STILL EVOLVI

Have culture and technology stopped evolution in its tracks?

Words by **Laura Mears**

"The genetic differences between us are surprisingly small"

Every human alive today can trace their ancestry back to east Africa around 200,000 years ago – DNA from a single woman still exists in every one of our cells. At the time, the human population was tiny, and her descendants are the only ones still alive today. They spread across the continent 100,000 years ago before radiating out in waves across the world. Scientists know the mother of humanity as mitochondrial Eve.

We may have dispersed, but the genetic differences between us are surprisingly small. There is no major distinction between people living on different continents or people of different races. In fact, there are more genetic differences between subspecies of chimpanzee. This similarity makes people question whether we've stopped evolving completely.

Evolution relies on a few key ingredients. Every generation, an organism makes more individuals than are able to survive. There are differences between those individuals, known as phenotypic variation. The cause of those differences, genes or genotype, are heritable, meaning that they can pass from one generation to the next. Some traits are better suited to the current environment than others. Individuals with those traits are more likely to survive and reproduce, passing the genes for their traits on to the next generation.

New traits enter populations in three main ways, the most well-known of which is mutation. When we make sperm or eggs, cells in our reproductive organs copy their DNA. This process is error-prone, so every time it happens mistakes creep in. This creates tiny changes in the genetic code that pass to the next generation. For the most part the differences don't do anything useful – or harmful. The mutations are often silent (they do nothing) or neutral (they do something, but it doesn't make a difference). In fact, many mutations aren't even in genes;

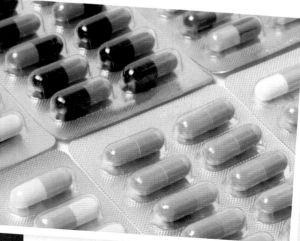

Modern medicine reduces the pressure of illness on our species

063

they're in the DNA that sits between them. However, sometimes mutations change the way a gene works.

New traits can also enter populations via gene flow. This happens when groups of people separate and then come back together, sharing new genetic information. Finally, traits change because of sex. Babies inherit genetic material from both parents, putting new combinations of genes together.

Over the past 100,000 years these three mechanisms have changed the traits that make us human, but we are still young in evolutionary terms. We take a long time to reproduce, and there's a limit to the amount of variation that can accumulate in a few hundred thousand years. Your genetic information only differs from mine by around 0.1 per cent, and most of those differences are single letter changes. Despite outward appearances, the whole human population still shares close family ties.

Our genes are always changing, but genetics is just one piece of the evolutionary puzzle. Our environment has a huge role to play in how our species evolves. For new traits to pass from generation to generation they need to change our chances of survival. This is where Darwin's

natural selection comes in. If a genetic change makes an individual more likely to reproduce they have a better chance of passing on their genes. We know this as 'survival of the fittest', but it's not always about being the biggest, strongest or fastest. It's about having traits that let you make the best use of your current environment. As the environment changes, so do the kind of mutations that might be useful.

This is where human evolution gets complicated. We can change our environment with culture, science and technology, messing with natural selection. If you look deep into history, our human-like ancestors were at the mercy of their environment. Lucy, a famous fossil of a species known as *Australopithecus afarensis*, lived 3.2 million years ago. She had ape-like characteristics, including a large jaw, long arms and a covering of fur, but she walked on two legs. She lived in the trees like other apes, but the environment was changing, trees were disappearing, and Lucy was spending more time on the ground. Eggs found near her remains suggest she might have been foraging.

Between Lucy and mitochondrial Eve, climate change eventually forced our ancestors out of the forests and onto the plains. They had to run

Agriculture gave us stable access to food, freeing up time for science

"Your genetic information only differs from mine by around 0.1 per cent"

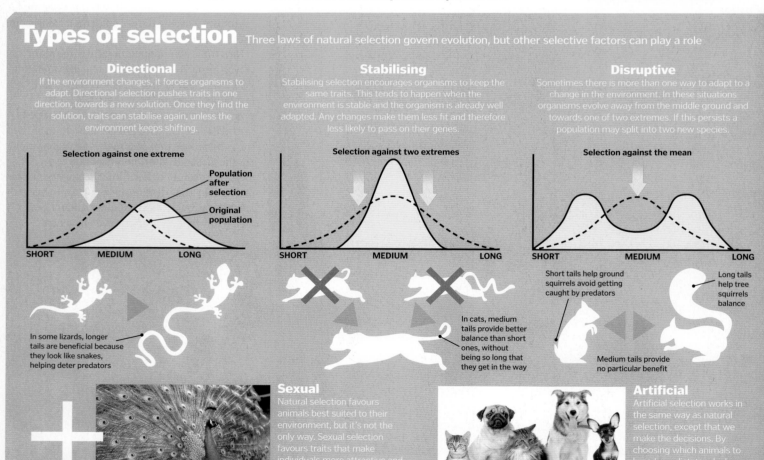

Types of selection
Three laws of natural selection govern evolution, but other selective factors can play a role

Directional
If the environment changes, it forces organisms to adapt. Directional selection pushes traits in one direction, towards a new solution. Once they find the solution, traits can stabilise again, unless the environment keeps shifting.

Selection against one extreme

Population after selection
Original population

SHORT   MEDIUM   LONG

In some lizards, longer tails are beneficial because they look like snakes, helping deter predators

Stabilising
Stabilising selection encourages organisms to keep the same traits. This tends to happen when the environment is stable and the organism is already well adapted. Any changes make them less fit and therefore less likely to pass on their genes.

Selection against two extremes

SHORT   MEDIUM   LONG

In cats, medium tails provide better balance than short ones, without being so long that they get in the way

Disruptive
Sometimes there is more than one way to adapt to a change in the environment. In these situations organisms evolve away from the middle ground and towards one of two extremes. If this persists a population may split into two new species.

Selection against the mean

SHORT   MEDIUM   LONG

Short tails help ground squirrels avoid getting caught by predators

Long tails help tree squirrels balance

Medium tails provide no particular benefit

Sexual
Natural selection favours animals best suited to their environment, but it's not the only way. Sexual selection favours traits that make individuals more attractive and more likely to reproduce, even if they don't help them to survive.

Artificial
Artificial selection works in the same way as natural selection, except that we make the decisions. By choosing which animals to breed, we dictate which traits are passed on to the next generation.

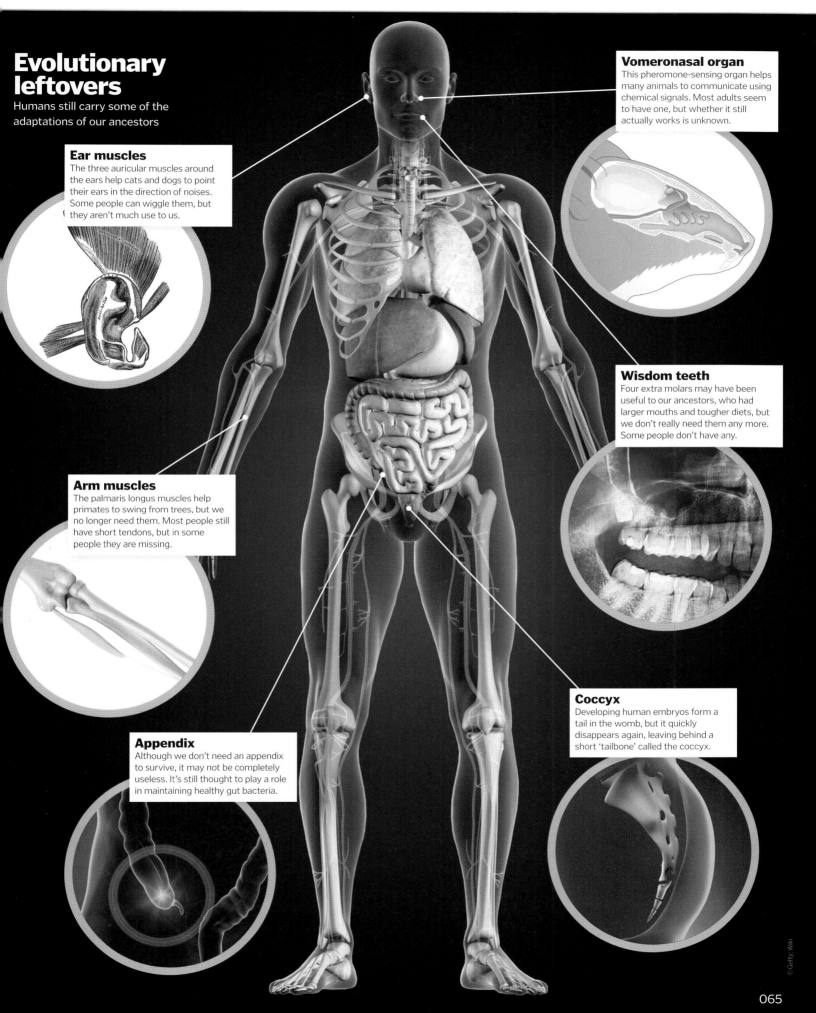

Evolutionary leftovers

Humans still carry some of the adaptations of our ancestors

Ear muscles
The three auricular muscles around the ears help cats and dogs to point their ears in the direction of noises. Some people can wiggle them, but they aren't much use to us.

Vomeronasal organ
This pheromone-sensing organ helps many animals to communicate using chemical signals. Most adults seem to have one, but whether it still actually works is unknown.

Arm muscles
The palmaris longus muscles help primates to swing from trees, but we no longer need them. Most people still have short tendons, but in some people they are missing.

Wisdom teeth
Four extra molars may have been useful to our ancestors, who had larger mouths and tougher diets, but we don't really need them any more. Some people don't have any.

Appendix
Although we don't need an appendix to survive, it may not be completely useless. It's still thought to play a role in maintaining healthy gut bacteria.

Coccyx
Developing human embryos form a tail in the womb, but it quickly disappears again, leaving behind a short 'tailbone' called the coccyx.

© Getty, Wiki

065

under blazing sunshine to survive, and body hair became a burden. Bare skin and the ability to lose heat by sweating became an advantage. Pressure from the environment pushed the genes of our ancestors to change.

Over time, early humans evolved bigger brains, smaller jaws and complex social structures. We harnessed fire and invented tools, and as we became more intelligent we made more and more changes to our environment. This changed everything.

The advent of agriculture around 10,000 years ago caused a seismic shift in human history. Suddenly, we could produce our own food on demand, right next to our homes. DNA from ancient humans has revealed that changing our own environment changed at least 12 regions of our genetic code.

Researchers at Harvard Medical School examined the remains of 230 people who lived between 8,500 and 2,300 years ago. They found differences in genes involved in height, metabolism and skin pigmentation. Around 4,000 years ago, a mutation appeared that allowed adults to keep digesting milk. Light skin became more common, which the researchers believe may have been a response to less vitamin D in a plant-based farmer's diet. The immune system also changed, which may have helped people to live closer together.

We share behaviours that we learn during our lifetimes, passing information from generation to generation like genes. Learning and culture change our environment, changing the pressures that drive selection. This kind of genetic and cultural co-evolution isn't unique to humans. Whales and dolphins are some of the most intelligent animals on the planet, and there is evidence that they also evolve in response to learning.

Killer whales can tackle many different types of prey, but certain groups prefer different meals. In the North Atlantic, for example, some like salmon, some prefer mammals, and others eat sharks. These cultural preferences pass from mother to baby, and because the groups don't tend to mix, they stay the same across generations. Scientists found differences in the genetics of whales that eat fish versus those that eat mammals. We changed our genes by learning to farm, and they've changed theirs by choosing which prey to eat.

This cultural learning helps us to keep adapting, but humans have taken it further than any other animal. We made clothes and complex shelters. We domesticated plants and animals to provide a steady source of food. We built boats, cars and planes to explore the world. We invented medicine to treat injuries and disease. We made it possible to choose when – and if – to have children. We can even survive in space. We have secured our environment, reducing the pressures that push other species to change over time. Reducing those pressures freed up even more time for new ideas and new technologies. Science has made it possible to change our environment more than ever before, but does that mean that we've stopped evolving?

It's hard to see evolution in action in human populations today because we have such a long lifespan, and even when natural selection isn't happening, our genes continue to mutate, a phenomenon known as genetic drift. However, there is one serious selective pressure that we still don't have under control: disease. If you look into its past you can see how modern humans have changed in recent years.

The plague ripped through Europe around 750 years ago, killing vast numbers of people. When our species faces diseases we can't yet treat,

Ongoing evolution

Two recent studies have found evidence to suggest that we are indeed still evolving, albeit very slowly. Among smokers, those with a variant of a gene known as CHRNA3 are associated with smoking more heavily than average. Being a heavy smoker increases the risk of dying from a smoking-related disease, such as lung cancer. Scientists found that, between generations of 80-year-olds and 60-year-olds, the variant of this gene has decreased by about one per cent. However, until further data is collected from younger generations, this trend cannot be confirmed.

A similar decline seems to be emerging in those with a variant of the gene ApoE4, which increases the risk of developing late-onset Alzheimer's and cardiovascular disease. One possible explanation for both these gene variants becoming rarer is that more people are having children later. The number of people waiting until their 40s or 50s to start a family is increasing, but this is also the age at which people with such gene variants may be at risk of dying.

Smokers with a variation in the CHRNA3 gene are more likely to be heavy smokers

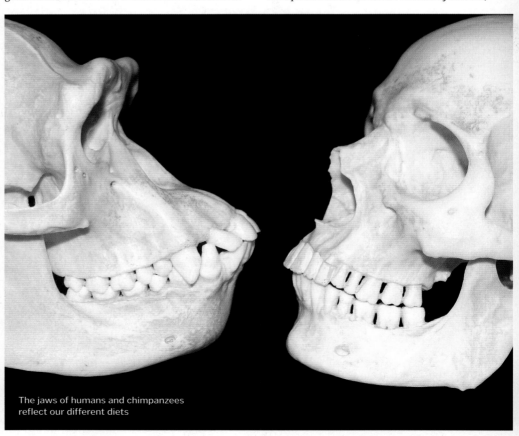

The jaws of humans and chimpanzees reflect our different diets

The development of technology will continue to shape the future of our species

Changes to our genes are only part of our evolutionary story

"Cultural learning helps us to keep adapting"

natural selection takes over. Scientists think that's why modern populations in Northern Europe have a higher frequency of a mutation in a gene called CCR5. This gene codes for a molecule used by the immune system, and it provides protection against the plague bacteria, *Yersinia pestis*. It also protects against the HIV virus. People with the protective trait were more likely to survive, and their descendants are still alive today.

As a species we have outsourced huge parts of our survival to technology. We control our environment to maintain a steady state, reducing the pressure that forces genes to change, but to keep this going we need our environment to stay the same, and we haven't worked it all out yet.

What happens when the climate changes, or when antibiotics no longer work as they should? We have buffered ourselves against natural selection for the moment, but we haven't out-evolved evolution.

Future humans

Work is underway to extend our understanding of evolution beyond the ideas set out by Darwin. It's not just genetic inheritance that affects our evolution; the environment that our parents pass on changes us too. In new environments different genes become more or less useful to our survival. By changing our environment we change the selective pressures that drive our species forward. In biology this process is known as niche construction.

Data suggests that cultural evolution has already changed the way that our genes evolved by affecting the type of selection we are under. Even so, our genes don't always need to change for our species to adapt. We can change our environment much more rapidly than we change our genes, allowing us to thrive in situations that our biology couldn't handle alone. Computer simulations suggest that this kind of cultural evolution could work in a similar way to genetic evolution, only faster. Who knows where that will take us as human culture continues to change and technology continues to improve.

What is a hernia?

Weakened muscles can lead to some serious side effects

Usually, your muscles are strong enough to hold your organs, but when they are weak it is possible that part of an organ can be pushed out through the wall of the cavity containing it, resulting in a hernia.

The most common type of hernia occurs when the intestines protrude through the abdominal muscle, leaving an unpleasant and often uncomfortable bump under the surface of the skin. Hernias can be caused when lifting heavy objects or by persistent coughing, and they are more common in older people.

Surgery can repair such injuries, pushing the bulge back into its correct place and strengthening the weakness in the muscle. However, complications can sometimes occur. Hernias around the intestines can obstruct the flow of the digestive tract, causing nausea and vomiting, or strangulation – a medical emergency that requires immediate attention if permanent damage is to be prevented.

> "Hernias can be caused when lifting heavy objects or by persistent coughing"

Strangulated hernia

A strangulated hernia is a medical emergency – immediate attention is needed to reduce the risk of permanent damage to the intestinal tract

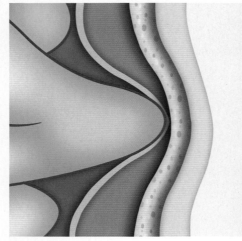

Weakened muscle
The abdominal wall weakens and becomes unable to hold the intestines in place effectively.

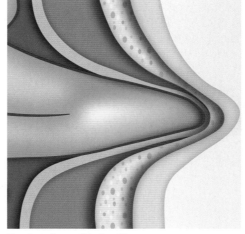

Protrusion of intestine
The intestines push outwards at a particularly weak point, often as a result of over-exertion of the muscle.

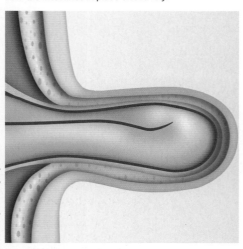

Intestines become trapped
A section of the intestines can become trapped by the surrounding tissue and unable to be pushed back inside.

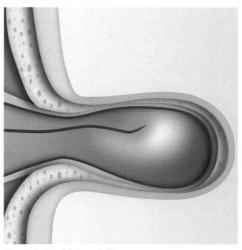

Restricted blood flow
The trapped section can become 'strangled' as its blood supply is cut off. This causes the trapped tissue to die, causing severe pain and requires urgent surgery.

Atomic energy levels

How atoms absorb or release energy depending on their electron arrangement

An atom's electrons orbit the nucleus at specific energy levels. The easiest way to imagine this concept is with a simplified atomic model, in which electrons orbit the nucleus like planets orbit a star.

Each defined orbit is known as an energy level. Electrons must have a certain amount of energy to orbit within each level, and this amount increases the further away an energy level is from the nucleus.

Electrons can gain or lose energy. If an electron absorbs enough energy to move up to the next energy level it is said to be in an excited state. The electrons in a substance can become excited if the matter is heated or if it absorbs pulses of electromagnetic radiation, such as light photons.

Being excited is an unstable state, so the electron eventually returns to its original, lower-energy level. This transition leads to the emission of a photon with the same amount of energy as the difference between the two energy levels it moves between.

The atoms of different elements have specific energy levels, so they will absorb and emit photons of different energies. Measuring the properties of photons absorbed or emitted by a substance can be used to identify what elements it contains.

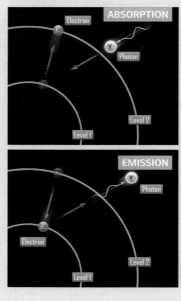

Absorbing a photon of a specific energy allows an electron to move to a higher energy level (top). When it eventually moves back to its original energy level, a photon is emitted (bottom).

How do we sense time?

The science behind why time flies when we're having fun

When you are waiting for a bus you can usually estimate how long you've been standing there. Our ability to keep track of time is important in almost every aspect of day-to-day life, from playing a musical instrument to holding a conversation.

That little internal alarm that says you've been standing in the shower for too long comes from a type of temporal processing supported by two neural clocks. Researchers previously thought that our intuitive timekeeping ability came from a part of the brain called the striatum. Studies have shown that this region is activated when people pay attention to time, and patients with Parkinson's disease – which disrupts the striatum – can have difficulty telling the time.

Scientists predict that the striatum consistently pulses with activity, a little bit like the ticking of a clock. However, recent studies suggest that in order to be conscious of the passage of time your brain also relies on the hippocampus to remember how many pulses

from the striatum have occurred. This concept is known as the interval timer theory, and it explains how we unconsciously judge time spans on the scale of seconds to hours.

You will notice that time spent with your friends seems to pass much faster than when you're writing an assignment. Neuroscientists have found that this is because your brain stops recording these pulses of activity when you stop paying attention to time, such as when you're engrossed in an activity. When this happens, the brain puts fewer 'ticks' of its internal clock in storage, making it feel like less time has passed.

On the other hand, in situations where you are more actively aware of the time – like when you're waiting for a delayed appointment – your mind will be counting every tick because you have little else to distract yourself with, making the passage of time feel much slower. So the next time you find that the day is dragging on, try to take your mind off the time to distract your internal clock.

If you want time to feel like it's flowing faster stop watching the clock!

Studies have found that the accuracy of our interval timers ranges from five to 60 per cent

Your brain's internal clock

The interval timer theory explains how your brain keeps time like a neurological metronome

3 Dopamine
A subtype of brain cells called spiny neurons monitor the cortical neurons' activity, keeping track of how many times their firing patterns repeat. When the event finishes – in this case, once the kettle has boiled – bursts of dopamine are sent towards the striatum.

4 Memory
The release of dopamine causes the spiny neurons to commit the firing pattern of the cortical neurons at that particular instant to memory. This creates a kind of 'time stamp' for the given event. Research suggests that there are unique memories for a whole range of different intervals.

5 Time's up
Now the spiny neurons have 'learned' these intervals they will monitor cortical firing rates until they match the memory for the time stamp that signals that particular event is over. Once this occurs the striatum sends signals to other areas of the brain involved in memory and decision making, giving you an internal 'time's up!' alert.

2 Synchronisation
This triggers specific cortical nerve cells (which usually fire at different speeds, shown in A) to briefly fire together at the same time (B). They then return to their original firing rates, but because they all started simultaneously their activity follows a particular pattern.

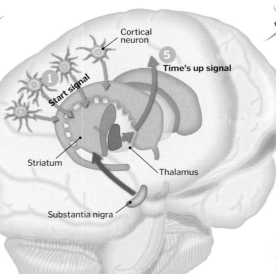

Cortical neuron

Time's up signal

Start signal

Spiny neuron

Striatum

Thalamus

Substantia nigra

1 Start the clock
A 'start' signal is activated by the onset of an event that lasts a familiar amount of time, such as the three minutes it takes to boil some water in a kettle.

© Illustration by The Art Agency/Andy Gauchie

EXPERIMENTS
THAT CHANGED THE
WORLD

The investigations that shaped science and provided the fundamental knowledge we rely on today

Words by **Scott Dutfield and Charlie Evans**

Cavendish weighs the world

England, 18th century

Not only did the solitary and eccentric Henry Cavendish discover hydrogen, but he also successfully measured the weight of the world. His ambitious experiment used a special piece of equipment called a torsion balance, and in 1798 he reported his results. By measuring the gravitational attraction between two different sized lead spheres, he calculated the Earth's density.

The apparatus consisted of an 1.8-metre wooden rod that had a 0.73-kilogram lead sphere attached to each end, suspended from a wire. A separate system of two larger 159-kilogram lead balls were placed close to the smaller balls. This

exerted enough gravitational force so that when the weights were tugged slightly the rod twists (a telescope was used to observe this). Cavendish performed his experiments in a dark and wind-proof to prevent any external air currents and temperature differences affecting his results. He was able to calculate the Earth's density by using the ratios of the forces between the spheres and the gravitational attraction of the Earth to the spheres.

Incredibly, his results were very accurate, and his great experiment meant we could also calculate the mass of the Sun and the Moon and even other planets in our Solar System.

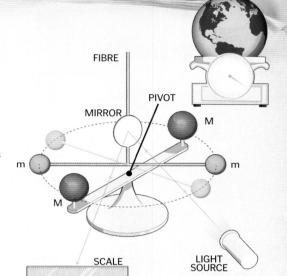

Cavendish's experiment to measure the weight of the world yielded results almost as accurate at today's calculations

Galileo Galilei and the Leaning Tower of Pisa Experiment

Italy, 16th century

Imagine you drop a bowling ball from one hand and a feather from the other. Which will fall faster? It is obviously the bowling ball, but this doesn't reflect the nature of the force of gravity.

Greek philosopher Aristotle had proposed that objects fell at different rates because gravity would act more strongly on heavier objects, but it turns out that the feather falls slower only because of air resistance. If you could perform the same experiment in a vacuum, the feather and ball will hit the ground at exactly the same time.

It is difficult to separate fact from legend, but the story goes that Aristotle's theory of gravity went unchallenged until Italian polymath Galileo Galilei disproved it. Though he spent the last years of his life imprisoned for going against the popular beliefs of the time, his work on speed, velocity, gravity and free fall provided the foundations of the understanding of how the planets and Solar System moved.

Hundreds of years after his death his experiment was repeated on the Moon – unsurprisingly, Galileo was right.

Cannonballs
Galileo took two cannonballs of different weights but with similar levels of air resistance.

Start of the race
He dropped both spheres from exactly the same height at exactly the same time.

Acceleration
Although they had different masses, the cannonballs fell at a very similar rate.

The finish line
The two balls hit the ground almost instantaneously. The difference in falling time (due to air resistance) was far less than the amount predicted by Aristotle's theory.

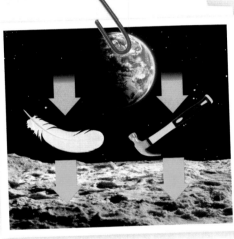

Apollo 15 commander David Scott replicated Galileo's experiment on the Moon in 1971

Galileo's cannonball experiment

Legend has it that Galileo climbed the Leaning Tower of Pisa to test his hypothesis

Under the near-vacuum on the Moon, the hammer and feather fell at the exact same rate

© Illustrators; Ed Crooks; Alamy; NASA

Mendel's peas

Czech Republic, 19th century

How do we inherit our genes from our parents? The answer was actually discovered not by studying humans but peas. Gregor Johann Mendel, an Augustinian friar, crossbred peas with differing characteristics in order to evaluate how different features were inherited in their offspring. His work focused on pea plants and their seven observable traits: the shapes of the pods and seeds; plant height; flower position; and seed, pod and flower colour.

The study took around eight years, in which time he observed some 28,000 pea plants. When looking at the colour of peas produced, Mendel found that different generations of plants expressed different ratios of green and yellow peas, with yellow being the dominant colour. He discovered that genes are paired and the mathematical pattern seen throughout generations caused their dominant and recessive expression. This pattern can also apply to the genetics that code for our eye and hair colour.

Mendel (back row, right-hand side) pictured here with his fellow monks

The generation game

How Mendel discovered genetic inheritance by playing with peas

Parents
Two true-bred plants with opposing physical characteristics (phenotype) were crossbred.

First generation
The first generation of peas expressed the dominant gene of one of its parents.

Second generation
This set of peas displayed a ratio of 3:1, three showing the dominant gene and one expressing the recessive gene.

Self-pollination
After the initial crossbreeding, peas were left to self-pollinate in order to explore a single lineage of genetics.

Rhazes and the hospital trial

Iraq, 10th century

Abu Bakr Muhammad ibn Zakariya al-Razi, known as Rhazes in the West, was a physician of many talents, including his novel approach in determining the location of a Baghdad hospital.

Under the instruction of the Caliph al-Muktafi to determine where the city's newest hospital should be built, Rhazes used meat to select the right spot. He travelled throughout the city hanging meat in potential locations and left them for a few days. The place in which the meat had experienced the least amount of decay was selected to be the location for the hospital, as he deduced that this was the cleanest area.

Rhazes was a talented polymath and wrote about many subjects

"He travelled throughout the city hanging meat in potential locations"

Penicillin is recognised as one of the world's most important advancements in medical history

Fleming's accidental discovery of penicillin

England, 20th century

In 1928, at St Mary's Hospital in London, Alexander Fleming was busy investigating the bacterium, *Staphylococcus aureus*. The bacteria had been wreaking havoc, causing fatal infections, and there was no medicine at the time to treat them.

On one occasion, Fleming forgot to put one of his Petri dishes into an incubator. While he was away on a two-week holiday the bacteria multiplied, and on his return he noticed something unusual in the rogue Petri dish. There was an area where the bacteria could not grow, and instead left a 'mould juice' to form a clear zone around itself. He investigated and found that the mould *Penicillium notatum* had contaminated the dish, inhibiting the growth of the bacteria.

In the late 1930s, scientists Howard Florey and Ernst Boris Chain had managed to isolate and purify penicillin, and the antibiotic was available as an injection by 1941. It is estimated that this discovery has saved up to 200 million lives to date.

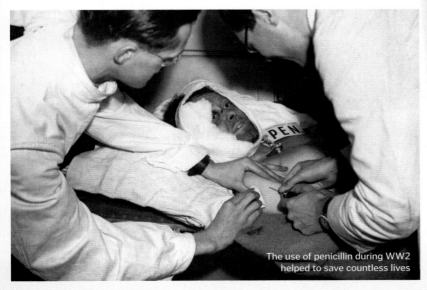

The use of penicillin during WW2 helped to save countless lives

Pasteur uncovers the origin of cells

France, 19th century

Back in the 1800s, people thought food spoiled and diseases were caused by 'bad air' or life spontaneously generating. Louis Pasteur didn't – he rejected the idea that mice could be randomly created from rotting wheat and old cloth over a few weeks.

After noticing that his own vats of beer were turning sour, Pasteur started analysing them only to discover they were swarming with bacteria. This convinced him that the spoiling of his brew was caused by these tiny microorganisms. He designed a simple experiment to prove his revolutionary germ theory, and as a result disproved the idea that cells could come from nothing.

So crucial was his work in the food and medicine industry that we even named a process after him – pasteurisation; the process of heat-treating something for a short time and cooling it down quickly to make it safe from bacteria.

Microbe matters

Armed with a set of swan-neck flasks, Louis Pasteur set out to challenge the status quo

The experiment
Two swan-neck flasks containing liquids filled with nutrients were boiled, to sterilise the liquid.

Straight-neck flask
The open flask allowed air and any bacteria to enter easily. The flask became murky with microbes growing in the liquid.

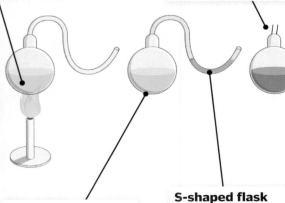

Success
Pasteur had proved that the organisms were not being spontaneously generated, and that it was the result of germs getting into the flask that causes the liquid to go off.

S-shaped flask
The flask's swan-neck shape meant that condensed liquid pooled in the bend, creating a seal so germs could not enter. The liquid did not change colour or become cloudy.

Marconi's wireless revolution

England, 20th century

We live in a world where we can communicate with almost anyone, anywhere. Amazingly, to do this we don't need to be plugged in. Wireless communication has changed the world.

Italian physicist Guglielmo Marconi was a pioneer in telecommunications; influenced by the recent discovery of electromagnetic waves, at the age of just 20 he successfully transmitted a wireless signal over a distance of more than 2.4 kilometres. He was fanatical about invention and wanted to create something practical and commercially successful from this technology.

In 1897, he took to the Salisbury Plains to pitch his workable system to the British government, which involved using an aerial held up by a balloon to improve the range of wireless transmission. When a Morse key was depressed it would cause a spark, which flowed up the antenna and radiated in all directions into space. As it spread through the air a second aerial connected to the receiver would pass over the coherer to complete the circuit and trigger a bell. He demonstrated that he could transmit this signal further than ever before without the need for wires. His next mission: transmit over open sea, and selected Lavernock Point, Wales as the site of the momentous experiment.

Marconi continued to develop the technology, and on 12 December, 1901, he sent the first long-range radio message some 3,380 kilometres across the Atlantic, between Poldhu, Cornwall, England and St John's, Newfoundland, Canada. The basis of all radio communication today had been invented, and though the equipment he used was not new, their organisation was.

"From my earliest experiments I had always held a belief that the day would come when mankind would be able to send messages without wires from between the further most ends of the Earth." How right Marconi was.

Marconi's first Transatlantic radio signal was sent from Cornwall to Newfoundland

Much of the technology we take for granted today only exists because of Marconi's work

Fermi's nuclear reactor

US, 20th century

After the atom was split and the term 'nuclear fission' was coined, physicist Enrico Fermi applied the principle to create the first self-sustaining nuclear chain reaction in a human made reactor: Chicago Pile-1.

Scientists were aware that a nuclear reactor would allow for the production of a weapon like nothing seen before. The outbreak of WWII meant that weapon production was a priority, a consequence of which was the birth of both the Manhattan Project and Fermi's reactor.

Once uranium-235 is hit with a neutron, the nucleus splits to form two smaller nuclei and more neutrons, which then go on to split other uranium atoms, thus forming a chain reaction. The reactor was made from stacks of graphite blocks to slow down fast uranium neutrons, increasing the likelihood of nuclear fission.

This reaction needed to be controlled in order for it to be safe. Control rods made from cadmium were used to absorb the excess neutrons created from the nuclear fission. Adding or removing the rods could control the longevity of the chain reaction. This reaction produced large amounts of energy, which could then be harnessed for warfare.

Chicago Pile-1 was built on a squash court at the University of Chicago

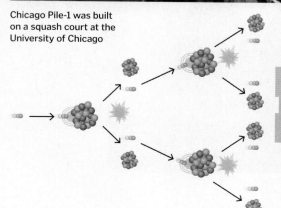

"Once uranium-235 is hit with a neutron, the nucleus splits to form two smaller nuclei and more neutrons"

Rutherford strikes gold

England, 20th century

It was previously believed that the structure of the atom was a sphere of positive charge housing smaller negatively charged electrons within it, like plums within a pudding. To test the accuracy of this 'plum pudding' model — under the direction of Ernest Rutherford — Hans Geiger and Ernest Marsden performed a series of experiments between 1908–1913 to prove Rutherford's theory of an atomic model, which resembled planets orbiting the Sun.

The physicists used a radioactive substance to bombard a thin piece of gold foil with positively charged alpha particles. The majority of particles passed through the foil without any deflection, suggesting that atoms had a great deal of open space. However, some were deflected off the gold foil at different angles, which meant that those particular particles had hit something with the same charge. This meant that rather than a positive charge engulfing electrons, a smaller positive charge was held in the dense middle, thus heralding the discovery of the atomic nucleus.

A whole new recipe
The experiment that disproved the plum pudding model

GOLD ATOMS

GOLD ATOMS

What Rutherford expected if Thomson's model were correct

What Rutherford actually observed

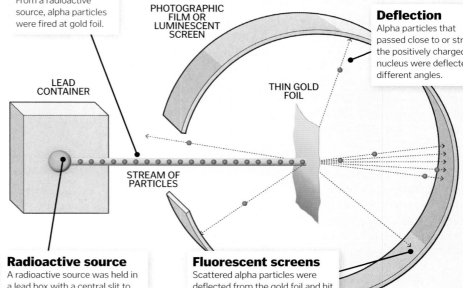

Alpha particles
From a radioactive source, alpha particles were fired at gold foil.

PHOTOGRAPHIC FILM OR LUMINESCENT SCREEN

Deflection
Alpha particles that passed close to or struck the positively charged nucleus were deflected at different angles.

LEAD CONTAINER

THIN GOLD FOIL

STREAM OF PARTICLES

Radioactive source
A radioactive source was held in a lead box with a central slit to allow particles to reach the foil.

Fluorescent screens
Scattered alpha particles were deflected from the gold foil and hit the zinc-sulphide-coated screens.

Lavoisier and the conservation of mass

France, 18th century

It was a French chemist named Antoine Lavoisier who formulated the concept of the conservation of mass – the idea that matter can neither be created nor destroyed, only rearranged. He did so by measuring the mass of reactants and products during chemical reactions.

One of Lavoisier's experiments entailed placing a burning candle inside a sealed glass jar. As the wick burned down and the candle melted, the weight of the jar and its contents remained the same, thereby proving his pioneering theory.

At the time, chemists were exploring the formation of calx (an oxide), predicting that metals lost mass as they were burnt. Lavoisier countered this with the idea that calx was the result of atmospheric gas interacting with the metal. Rather than the metal losing mass, he found it gained weight by combining with oxygen from the air.

Transforming matter
The experiment that changed our understanding of matter without tipping the scales

Heat source
The sealed tin was left to form calx (metallic ash) within the sealed jar, heated by focussing the Sun's rays with a magnifying glass.

Sealed jar
Tin was placed under a sealed jar to ensure that no gas could enter or escape.

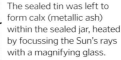

TIN IN A SEALED GLASS VESSEL

WHITE POWDER IN A SEALED GLASS VESSEL

Weight
After the calx had formed the scale showed that the tin had not gained or lost any weight/mass.

Lind cures sailors' scurvy

HMS Salisbury, 18th century

Bleeding gums, your teeth dropping out, weak limbs, swollen legs and nasty patches of blood under your skin – a pirate's life probably wouldn't have been ideal for most of us. Scurvy was one of the diseases that plagued pirates and sailors in the early days of seafaring. We know today that the disease is caused by a serious lack of vitamin C, something we need to form collagen, a vital component in structural and supportive connective tissue. Without enough collagen, the blood vessels and bones of those with scurvy break down until they suffer a slow and painful death. But in the time of Scottish physician James Lind, there was no knowledge about these tiny nutrients. People thought that scurvy might be contagious or caused by madness.

In 1747, Lind started one of the world's first clinical trials. He suspected that acids could help stop the putrefaction of the body, and he devised a trial to test different ways of introducing certain acids into people's diets. He divided a group of 12 scurvy-ridden sailors into six groups of two, all of which were to eat the same diet as one another but with the addition of an acidic supplement.

Each group was treated with either a quart of cider, 25 drops of elixir of vitriol, two spoonfuls of vinegar, half a pint of seawater, two oranges and one lemon, or a spice paste, every day. After six days most of the sailors eating the fruit had made an almost complete recovery. While Lind was on the wrong track about the cause of the disease, he had found the cure.

Scurvy is a disease that people around the world still suffer from, particularly in areas of war or famine

The solar eclipse allowed Eddington to observe how the light from stars is affected by the gravity of the Sun

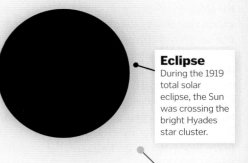

Apparent positions
Eddington and his team took pictures during the eclipse and compared the stars' positions to initial measurements taken previously.

Eclipse
During the 1919 total solar eclipse, the Sun was crossing the bright Hyades star cluster.

Gravitational lensing
As Einstein's theory predicted, the path of light from distant stars was 'bent' by our Sun's gravity.

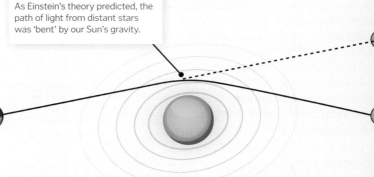

Eddington and the eclipse

Africa, 20th century

Scientific explanations in theoretical physics often remain just that, theoretical – but not all of them do. Albert Einstein published his general theory of relativity back in 1915, a criteria of which was that light bends near a massive gravitational force. However, Einstein was aware that should this or any of the other criteria required to support his revolutionary idea be disproven, then bang went the theory.

Einstein's pioneering work remained a theory until an astronomer named Sir Arthur Eddington used an eclipse to prove light could be bent by gravitational forces. In order for Einstein's theory to be correct, Eddington had to prove that the light had been bent by a source of intense gravity, such as the Sun. A total solar eclipse in 1919 presented Eddington with a unique opportunity to witness the night sky during the daytime.

After setting sail to Príncipe Island to get the best view of a predicted solar eclipse and test out Einstein's theory, Eddington observed the locations of stars at night and then again under the false night of an eclipse. This meant that he could observe if the gravity of the Sun had altered the stars' apparent positions, which in fact it had. This proved that light had been bent on its journey to Earth by way of the Sun's gravity, meaning Einstein was correct.

The creation of graphene

England, 21st century

In 2004, Professors Andre Geim and Konstantin Novoselov were experimenting with a graphite crystal. They removed some graphite flakes using sticky tape and, upon closer inspection, realised that some of the flakes were thinner than others.

So they repeated the process, taking off more layers from the original peeled-off flake. Amazingly, their method worked. Each time the flakes were thinner, and they eventually managed to create flakes that were only one carbon atom thick. Although the existence of graphene had been predicted, no one knew how to isolate it. Until now.

It sounds simple, but graphene has turned out to be a really important material and just what we needed in this digital age for display screens and electric/photonic circuits. A fantastic conductor of heat, dense, lightweight, flexible and transparent, it has been used in everything from tyres to transistors.

> "Graphene has turned out to be a really important material in this digital age"

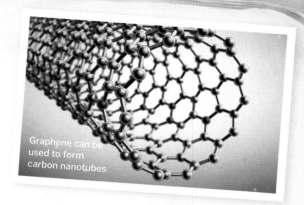

Graphene can be used to form carbon nanotubes

Making one layer of graphite

Repetition and patience was key to creating the strongest material known to man

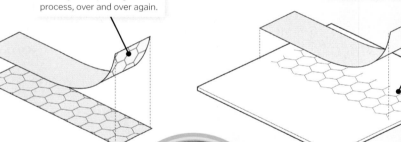

Sticky tape
The scientists used sticky tape to remove a thin layer of graphite.

Graphite
A block of graphite was being used to study the properties of the material.

A new method
The scientists noticed that the flakes were of different thickness. They decided to investigate, repeating the process, over and over again.

Simple but effective
Geim and Novoselov transfer the sample onto a silicon surface, successfully isolating graphene.

From theory to reality

Switzerland, 21st century

In 1964, particle physicist Peter Higgs proposed a theory as to how particles have mass. He suggested that empty space is occupied by a field termed the Higgs field, where particles pass through it and either collect mass, like an electron, or don't interact with it at all and remain massless, such as a photon. An analogy would be a person moving through a crowd of strangers versus a crowd of friends.

Moving through of crowd of strangers, you would pass easily without stopping, whereas surrounded by friends you might stop to talk, taking you longer to make your way through. In this case your friends would be the Higgs boson. The Large Hadron Collider fires two beams of protons in opposite directions and accelerates them to near the speed of light so they collide to release the boson and other subatomic particles. This became a reality on 4 July 2012.

Higgs boson

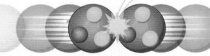

Proton collision

Higgs received the Nobel Prize in Physics in 2013 for his theoretical discovery

Why you lose your voice

What causes your speech to become croaky?

There are a number of reasons why you may lose your voice, but the most common cause is an illness known as laryngitis. This occurs when the vocal cords in your voice box become irritated or swollen, affecting the way they produce sound. Laryngitis itself has many possible causes, including infection from a virus, such as a cold or the flu; allergies to things like dust or fumes; or straining your voice from singing or shouting for long periods. The inflammation of your vocal cords will usually get better by itself within one or two weeks with plenty of vocal rest and fluids.

The effects of laryngitis

Discover how this common illness affects your speech

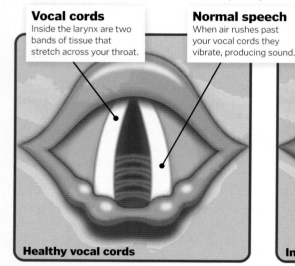

Vocal cords
Inside the larynx are two bands of tissue that stretch across your throat.

Normal speech
When air rushes past your vocal cords they vibrate, producing sound.

Healthy vocal cords

Inflamed vocal cords

Croaky voice
When your vocal cords are swollen they don't vibrate as easily, affecting your speech.

Larynx (voice box)
Your voice is generated in this tube of cartilage that sits at the top of your windpipe.

What is dry ice?

Dry ice changes from a solid to a gas in a process called sublimation

The secret to creating a spooky fog with CO_2

Popular in scary movies and big-budget stage productions, dry ice is a very different substance to the cubes of frozen water that keep your drink cold. Instead of H_2O, dry ice is actually the solid form of CO_2, or carbon dioxide, the gas we breathe out and plants use to photosynthesise. CO_2 freezes into a solid at -78 degrees Celsius (much lower than the temperature at which water freezes) and when it reaches room temperature it turns directly from a solid into a gas rather than a liquid. Not only is this useful for creating an atmospheric fog; it is also great for keeping things refrigerated on long journeys. By packing food in dry ice, it can be kept cool in transit without there being a messy puddle of water when it reaches its final destination.

Creating dry ice is a little more difficult than just freezing water. First you have to cool and pressurise CO_2 gas to turn it into a liquid, then depressurise it so it expands back into a gas. This causes a rapid temperature drop that freezes the gas into solid dry ice.

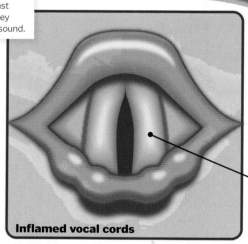

The higher the percentage of DHA in the lotion, the darker your tan will be

How does fake tan work?

The clever chemistry behind the lotions that give you a sun-kissed look

f you're looking for a golden tan but don't have the time – or weather – to bask in the Sun's rays, then you might prefer to fake it instead. Tanning lotions contain the chemical dihydroxyacetone (DHA), which creates a browning reaction when applied to the skin – the same reaction that causes bacon to change colour when it's cooked. The effect is gradual, taking around two to four hours to work, and it only lasts for up to ten days because it fades as your dead skin cells shed. Some fake tans may also contain erythrulose, another chemical with a more gradual browning effect, and sunblock to protect against the Sun's UV rays.

A tan in a bottle
What happens when you apply fake tan to your skin?

Application
Dihydroxyacetone in the lotion reacts with amino acids in the top layer of your skin.

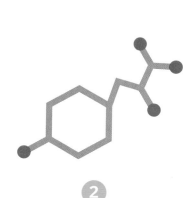

Chemical reaction
Chemicals called melanoidins are produced through a Maillard reaction, the same type of reaction responsible for browning cooked meat.

Golden tan
The structure of the melanoidins means they absorb certain wavelengths of light, making your skin appear tanned.

What are smelling salts?

Discover how a quick sniff can revive you from unconsciousness

Although smelling salts were more commonly used in Victorian times to bring people round after they had fainted, they are still sometimes used today by athletes looking to boost their alertness. Traditionally they are made from a mixture of strong-smelling ammonium carbonate crystals and perfume, which helps to mask the unpleasant smell, but modern varieties can be made from ammonia dissolved in water and ethanol. They work by releasing ammonia gas, which when breathed in irritates the membranes of the nose and lungs. This triggers the body's natural reflex to inhale air, helping to increase the flow of oxygen to the brain, either waking you up or making you feel more alert.

Despite the name, smelling salts do not contain sodium chloride, the type of salt we use to flavour food, but they were once used in cooking. In the 19th century, before the arrival of baking powder and baking soda, ammonium carbonate was used to make bread and cakes rise. It's still used in a few traditional Scandinavian recipes today.

Although relatively harmless in small doses, inhaling large amounts of ammonia can cause lung damage

© Alamy, Getty

079

FOOD WASTE

Follow the food that goes uneaten on the journey from field to fork

How many times have you bought some fresh fruit just for it to end up in the bin just days later, or emptied your leftovers into the bin? It happens to the best of us – impulse buying, improper planning and being forgetful means a large amount of the food we buy goes uneaten. But the biggest cause for concern when we're thinking about food waste is what happens between the produce growing on the field and arriving at your kitchen. It is estimated that between a third and a half of all food produced never makes its way onto a plate.

THE JOURNEY OF AGRICULTURAL FOOD WASTE

Losses occur at all stages of the food supply chain, from production to consumption

INITIAL QUANTITY
According to a UN report from 2011, approximately 4 billion tons of food is produced globally each year, but one-third of this ends up going to waste.

AGRICULTURE
The first losses in food production occur due to infestations of pests and microorganisms, as well as agricultural machines that are unable to harvest an entire crop efficiently. Diseased livestock and fish bycatch also lead to losses.

POST-HARVEST
After harvest, many items of produce can end up getting damaged or destroyed while in storage or being transported due to temperature and humidity changes or the presence of microorganisms and pests.

PROCESSING
Edible food can end up going to waste in factories and processing plants. This can include the skin of 'ready-peeled' veg or trimmings of meat, as well as products that have been contaminated or don't conform to standards.

DISTRIBUTION
Retailers usually have strict standards for how produce must look; items may not be put on the shelves if they have bruising or are unusually shaped. Stores may also reject food deliveries if they have surplus stock already.

CONSUMPTION
Large portion sizes at home and in restaurants, as well as misunderstanding 'best-before' labels, means a significant amount of good food is thrown away at the consumer end of the food production chain.

GRAINS — DEVELOPED / DEVELOPING: 65%, 78.5%, 14%, 3.5%, 1.5%, 1.5%, 7.5%, 4%, 7.5%, 7%, 4.5%, 5.5%

ROOTS / TUBERS — DEVELOPED / DEVELOPING: 49.5%, 57%, 7%, 1.5%, 3%, 3.5%, 5.5%, 3.5%, 7%, 20.5%, 28%, 14%

OILS / BEANS — DEVELOPED / DEVELOPING: 80%, 68.5%, 0.5%, 7%, 3%, 5%, 11%, 0.5%, 8%, 5.5%, 1%, 10%

FRUIT / VEG — DEVELOPED / DEVELOPING: 67.5%, 46.5%, 6%, 10.5%, 2.5%, 12.5%, 12%, 5.5%, 0.5%, 4%, 10%, 22.5%

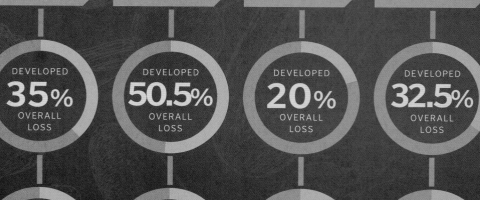

GRAINS — DEVELOPED **35%** OVERALL LOSS — DEVELOPING **21.5%** OVERALL LOSS

ROOTS / TUBERS — DEVELOPED **50.5%** OVERALL LOSS — DEVELOPING **43%** OVERALL LOSS

OILS / BEANS — DEVELOPED **20%** OVERALL LOSS — DEVELOPING **31.5%** OVERALL LOSS

FRUIT / VEG — DEVELOPED **32.5%** OVERALL LOSS — DEVELOPING **53.5%** OVERALL LOSS

FOOD WASTE SOLUTIONS

Better labelling

There is often confusion around what the 'use-by', 'sell-by' and 'best before' dates on packaging mean, so consumers often throw away food that was good to eat. Using 'spoils on' dates rather than using a sell-by date could mean that markets can keep produce on the shelves longer.

Food distribution

Overstocked stores can help to reduce waste by redistributing their surplus stock. They can send any extra food they don't need to food banks, community fridges and similar schemes. There are even apps that can help – Food Cowboy helps connect companies donating spare food with those who need it.

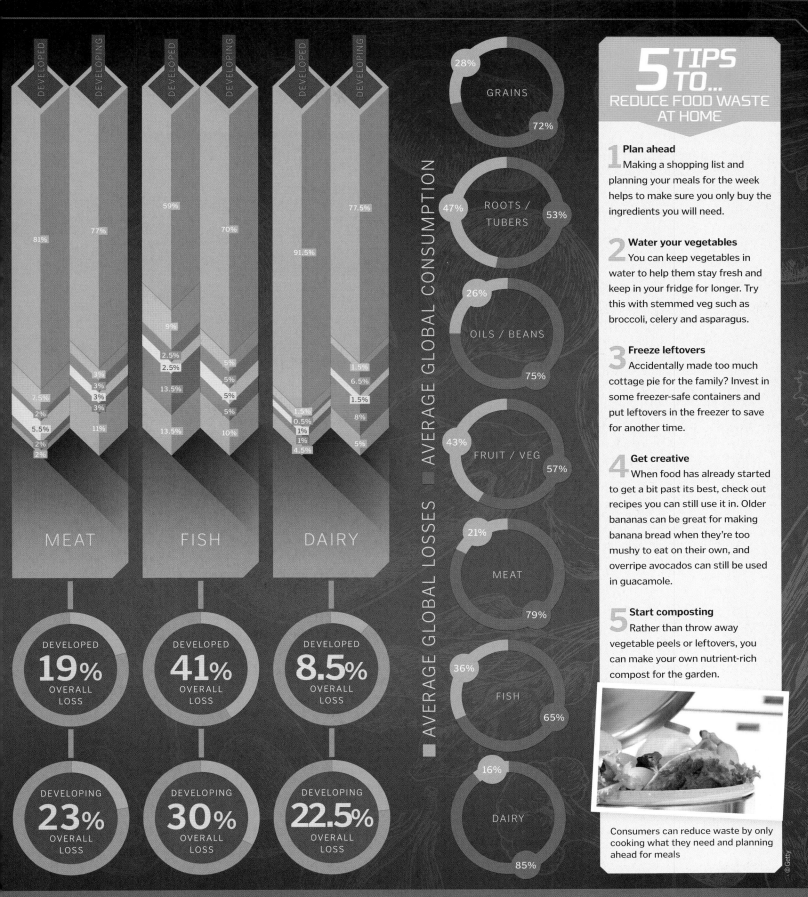

DEVELOPED · DEVELOPING · DEVELOPED · DEVELOPING · DEVELOPED · DEVELOPING

MEAT

- 81%
- 77%
- 7.5%
- 3%
- 3%
- 2%
- 3%
- 5.5%
- 11%
- 2%
- 2%

FISH

- 59%
- 70%
- 9%
- 2.5%
- 2.5%
- 5%
- 13.5%
- 5%
- 5%
- 5%
- 13.5%
- 10%

DAIRY

- 77.5%
- 91.5%
- 1.5%
- 6.5%
- 1.5%
- 1.5%
- 0.5%
- 1%
- 1%
- 4.5%
- 8%
- 5%

MEAT
| DEVELOPED **19%** OVERALL LOSS | DEVELOPING **23%** OVERALL LOSS |

FISH
| DEVELOPED **41%** OVERALL LOSS | DEVELOPING **30%** OVERALL LOSS |

DAIRY
| DEVELOPED **8.5%** OVERALL LOSS | DEVELOPING **22.5%** OVERALL LOSS |

■ AVERAGE GLOBAL CONSUMPTION   ■ AVERAGE GLOBAL LOSSES

GRAINS — 28% / 72%

ROOTS / TUBERS — 47% / 53%

OILS / BEANS — 26% / 75%

FRUIT / VEG — 43% / 57%

MEAT — 21% / 79%

FISH — 36% / 65%

DAIRY — 16% / 85%

5 TIPS TO... REDUCE FOOD WASTE AT HOME

1 Plan ahead
Making a shopping list and planning your meals for the week helps to make sure you only buy the ingredients you will need.

2 Water your vegetables
You can keep vegetables in water to help them stay fresh and keep in your fridge for longer. Try this with stemmed veg such as broccoli, celery and asparagus.

3 Freeze leftovers
Accidentally made too much cottage pie for the family? Invest in some freezer-safe containers and put leftovers in the freezer to save for another time.

4 Get creative
When food has already started to get a bit past its best, check out recipes you can still use it in. Older bananas can be great for making banana bread when they're too mushy to eat on their own, and overripe avocados can still be used in guacamole.

5 Start composting
Rather than throw away vegetable peels or leftovers, you can make your own nutrient-rich compost for the garden.

Consumers can reduce waste by only cooking what they need and planning ahead for meals

©Getty

Improving policy
Significant amounts of fruit and vegetables are lost due to industry standards that focus on the appearance of the item rather than its quality. Improving policies surrounding which items are thrown out due to aesthetics would reduce unnecessary waste.

Consumer choices
Consumer choices impact the food supply chain. If we all take steps to reduce waste as individuals – by selecting 'wonky veg' or using up our leftovers instead of throwing them away – it will make a significant difference.

Building infrastructure
Improving current food harvesting methods, storage and transport facilities and processing techniques will make a big difference to the amount of food that is lost at almost every stage of food production.

TRANSPORT

084
Supersonic stealth jets

092
The Trans-Siberian Railway

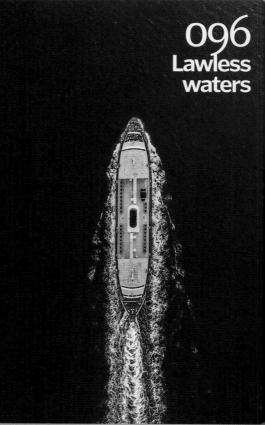

096
Lawless waters

097
The history of tarmacadam

Véritable Extrait de Viande LIEBIG.

LE MACADAM.

098
Rocket travel

"By 2023, getting around the world in 80 minutes may not be quite quick enough"

SUPER
STEALT

SONIC JETS

HOW THE FIFTH GENERATION OF FIGHTER AIRCRAFTS WILL CONQUER THE SKIES

Words by **Jonny O'Callaghan**

We've come a long way from the Wright brothers. Their first powered flight in 1903 consisted of a rudimentary wooden glider powered by propellers that reached a modest speed of 43 kilometres per hour. Now, more than a century later, a fleet of advanced supersonic stealth fighter jets are taking to the skies, capable of going undetected by radar and reaching speeds far in excess of the speed of sound – Mach 1 – which is around 1,235 kilometres per hour depending on air pressure and temperature.

The US was the first country to develop a so-called fifth-generation fighter with its F-22 aircraft, loosely defined as being a jet that has advanced stealth capabilities despite being armed, sleek designs to carve through the air and the capability of cruising at supersonic speeds without the use of fuel-hungry afterburners. But while the US currently dominates the field, Russia and China are quickly making headway, and many are already excited about what's next on the horizon, with artificial intelligence and autonomous flight all expected to play a part in the future of fighters.

Stealth fighter jets are iconic in their design and capabilities. They can enable rapid response to conflict, striking targets while remaining almost completely undetected. Their smooth and sleek bodies hide powerful weaponry under their skin, with the jets designed to have as few obtrusive parts as possible to give them a low radar cross-section (RCS). Powerful engines enable speeds of up to Mach 2, and pilots are given advanced helmets and technologies to help them locate and destroy targets.

> "AI and autonomous flight are expected to play a part in future"

The US F-22 has been operational since 2005, but we've recently also seen the American F-35 – delayed by more than a decade and significantly over budget – enter service in 2015. The start of 2018, meanwhile, has seen both Russia and China's first stealth fighter jets; the Su-57 and J-20 respectively. Other countries including India, Japan and Turkey are now developing their own such vehicles as a new wave of advanced warfare takes place in the skies.

Over the next few pages we've run through some of the major players in stealth fighter jet technology and outlined some of the key features that make them so formidable. The Wright brothers may have changed the world with their fateful flight, but as the saying goes, you ain't seen nothing yet.

F-22 RAPTOR vs F-35 LIGHTNING II

These American fighters are all but unmatched in the skies

At first glance, these two planes look quite similar, but beneath their exteriors lies very different technology. The F-22 Raptor, developed by Lockheed Martin and Boeing, has been in service since 2005, billed as the world's first stealth air-to-air fighter. Its curved body scatters incoming radio waves, ensuring the plane does not appear on scanners, and its weapons can be carried inside the fuselage, so it doesn't have any errant parts that might give its position away. It's capable of speeds of up to around Mach 2 and was the first US fighter able to 'supercruise', which means it can fly at supersonic speeds without using its afterburner, managing an impressive Mach 1.5 in this mode. This is thanks to two Pratt & Whitney F119-PW-100 engines.

Lockheed Martin's F-35 Lightning II Joint Strike Fighter (JSF), meanwhile, has a maximum speed of Mach 1.6. There are three variants: the F-35A, F-35B and F-35C, each with slightly different abilities. While it can't officially supercruise, it can maintain a speed of Mach 1.2 without its afterburners for a brief time, and like the F-22 it's designed to scatter radar waves and remain invisible on radar screens. It's outfitted with a single Pratt & Whitney F135 engine and, despite the delays, it's been described as one of the most advanced aircraft in the world. It's more suited to air-to-ground combat than the F-22, being able to carry more powerful bombs. Although it flew for the first time in 2006, it didn't enter service until 2015.

> "The F-35 is one of the most advanced aircraft in the world"

Fibre mat
The plane is built with absorbent materials, such as fibre mat, to give it a low radar profile.

Battle of the beasts
How these two advanced aircraft stack up against one other

F-22 KEY STATS

Length	18.9m
Wingspan	13.6m
Max range	2,960km
Top speed	Mach 2+

Heat
Horizontal fins at the rear of the aircraft hide the heat signature from its twin engines.

Wings
The edges of the front and rear wings line up so they are less noticeable on radar.

Supercruise
The F-22 can supercruise at Mach 1.5, meaning it doesn't need to use its afterburners and waste more fuel.

Lt Col. Anita Coomansingh Pang

Hidden weapons
The F-22 can carry weapons in its fuselage so they don't stick out and ruin its stealth capability.

F-22 RAPTOR

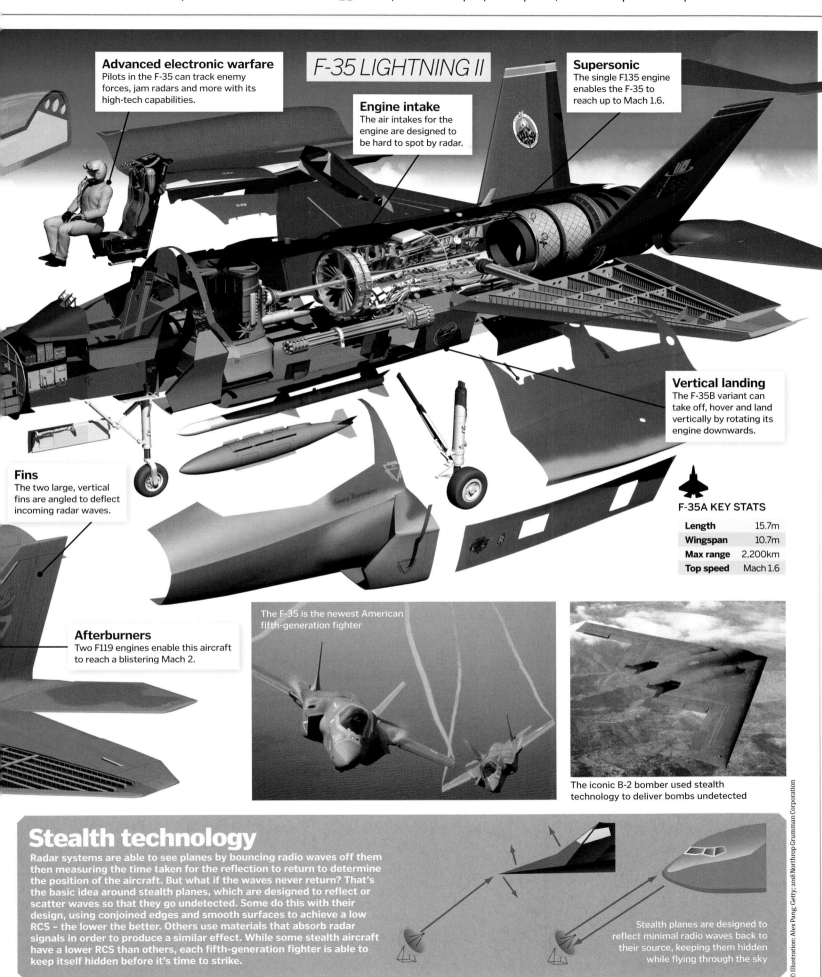

F-35 LIGHTNING II

Advanced electronic warfare
Pilots in the F-35 can track enemy forces, jam radars and more with its high-tech capabilities.

Engine intake
The air intakes for the engine are designed to be hard to spot by radar.

Supersonic
The single F135 engine enables the F-35 to reach up to Mach 1.6.

Vertical landing
The F-35B variant can take off, hover and land vertically by rotating its engine downwards.

Fins
The two large, vertical fins are angled to deflect incoming radar waves.

Afterburners
Two F119 engines enable this aircraft to reach a blistering Mach 2.

F-35A KEY STATS

Length	15.7m
Wingspan	10.7m
Max range	2,200km
Top speed	Mach 1.6

The F-35 is the newest American fifth-generation fighter

The iconic B-2 bomber used stealth technology to deliver bombs undetected

Stealth technology

Radar systems are able to see planes by bouncing radio waves off them then measuring the time taken for the reflection to return to determine the position of the aircraft. But what if the waves never return? That's the basic idea around stealth planes, which are designed to reflect or scatter waves so that they go undetected. Some do this with their design, using conjoined edges and smooth surfaces to achieve a low RCS – the lower the better. Others use materials that absorb radar signals in order to produce a similar effect. While some stealth aircraft have a lower RCS than others, each fifth-generation fighter is able to keep itself hidden before it's time to strike.

Stealth planes are designed to reflect minimal radio waves back to their source, keeping them hidden while flying through the sky

SUKHOI SU-57

How does Russia's first stealth fighter stand up to the American's?

The Su-57 is Russia's first operational stealth fighter

Russia's Su-57 (also known as the PAK FA Tu-50), developed by manufacturer Sukhoi, recently came into service when it was deployed to Syria in February 2018. The aircraft, billed as a fifth-generation fighter, is the first Russian aircraft to employ stealth technology. Like the F-22, this plane is designed to scatter and deflect radar waves, using sawtooth edges and angled wings to keep the plane out of radar sight. The Su-57 can reach an impressive Mach 2 using a

pair of Type 117 engine, and it can supercruise at Mach 1.6. This makes it faster than both the F-22 and F-35.

Like those two planes, the Su-57 carries its weapons in hidden bays, keeping it invisible to radar. It also uses radar-absorbing and radar-shielding materials and coatings to reduce its RCS, in addition to radar blockers. The cockpit and pilot's radar signature are kept small, meanwhile, with a special coating on the canopy

of the plane. However, the Su-57 has come under some criticism for still having an RCS of 0.3 to 0.5 square metres, compared to just 0.0001 and 0.001 square metres for the F-22 and F-35 respectively, meaning its stealth capabilities are perhaps not as impressive. Nonetheless, it is a formidable aircraft, with a top speed that can't be bested by its American counterparts.

Inside the Su-57

The technology that may allow Russia to rival the US in the sky

KEY STATS

Length	22m
Wingspan	14.2m
Max range	3,500km
Top speed	Mach 2

High flier
The Su-57 is able to reach an altitude of up to 20,000 metres.

Long range operations
The Su-57 boasts a maximum range of up to 3,500 kilometres – significantly farther than the F-22 and F-35.

Engines
A pair of Type 117 engines propel the plane up to speeds of around Mach 2.

It costs around $50 million (£36 million) to build a single Su-57 jet

Engine spacing
The Su-57's engines are deliberately spaced wide apart so as to accommodate a larger internal weapons bay.

A senior Russian official has stated that the Su-57 could be upgraded to become a 6th-generation fighter

"The Su-57 can reach Mach 2 and supercruise at Mach 1.6, making it faster than the F-22 and F-35"

Size
At 22 metres long, and with a wingspan of 14.2 metres, the jet is slightly on the large side for a fighter jet.

Cockpit
The cockpit is covered in a coating to hide the radar signature of the pilot.

Missile sensor
Located behind the cockpit, the upper-hemisphere missile approach warning will alert the pilot to incoming missiles.

Chengdu J-20

China's foray into the world of fifth-generation fighters is the somewhat mysterious Chengdu J-20 stealth fighter, developed by the Chengdu Aerospace Corporation. It is China's first stealth fighter, capable of achieving speeds of up to Mach 2. The J-20 is powered by two turbofan engines with afterburn capabilities, with three internal bays in its fuselage to hide weapons. It's believed to have field signature reduction technology that helps keep it hidden. It's shaped in a similar way to the F-22 to minimise its radar signature, although some doubts have been raised about its engine nozzles, which may expose it to radar. It flew for the first time in 2011 but officially entered service in September 2017, making it the world's fourth fifth-generation stealth fighter.

© Illustration: Adrian Mann; Getty; Shutterstock; WIKI/Toshi Aoki/Vitaly V Kuzmin

Hidden arms
Like the F-22 and F-35, the Su-57 keeps its weapons hidden.

Cloaking coating
The plane is coated in radar-absorbing and radar-shielding materials.

Many features of the Chengdu J-20 are still largely unknown

The Chengdu J-20 is one of two fighter jets being developed in China

Stealth silhouette
The edges of the plane are aligned to reduce its radar signature.

FUTURE STEALTH FIGHTERS

What can we expect from the next generation of advanced jets?

Some of the aircraft on these pages may have wowed you so far, but in the future we're promised even more impressive technologies leading up to the sixth generation of fighters. Some of these will include advanced artificial intelligence and may even be operated without a human pilot onboard as countries around the world aim to modernise their air forces.

These aircraft will boast extended ranges to strike distant locations, and some may even include a second pilot to coordinate a fleet of additional unmanned vehicles. Others may have sensors built into the skin of the aircraft to hide them from radar view, while some could even possess hypersonic weaponry – those that can reach or exceed Mach 5.

One particularly impressive plane in development is the Taranis from BAE Systems in the UK. This uncrewed vehicle flew for the first time in 2013, and its technology is designed around intercontinental missions. Controlled by a human on the ground, it is capable of speeds of more than Mach 1 – but it's the remote control aspect that really makes it a fearsome future weapon. Yet while it boasts stealth technology alongside its supersonic capabilities, it won't see combat itself. Instead, a successor will be developed to enter service in the 2030s that will incorporate its technologies.

Boeing, meanwhile, is hard at work on a sixth-generation fighter as part of its F/A-XX programme. As yet unnamed and mostly under wraps, we do know the jet will have no tail and will sport a similar sensor system to the F-35. It's designed to be both fast and stealthy, with its wings angled almost like a rhombus to reduce its radar signature. It's hoped that it will enter service at some point in the 2030s, replacing the US Navy's Super Hornet aircraft.

Then there's the B-21 Raider, a stealth bomber being designed by the US company Northrup Grumman. It's not known yet if it will be supersonic, but we do know it's designed to be able to deliver precision strikes anywhere in the world. It will have a bat-like wing design and stealth capabilities to keep it hidden. Early versions are likely to be crewed, but it's possible there could be uncrewed versions in the future.

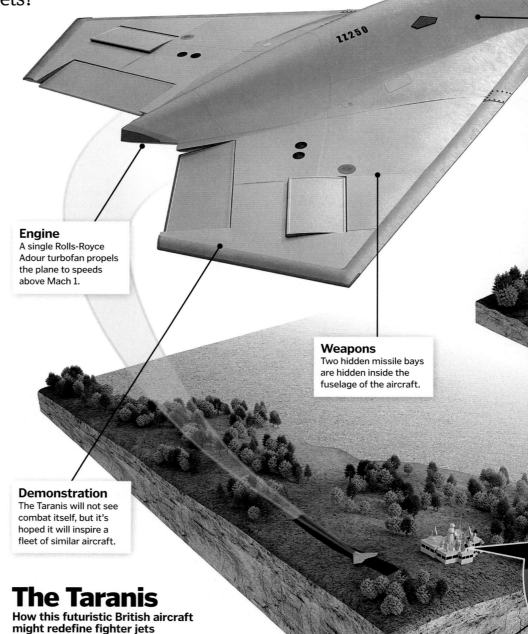

Stealth
The sleek, angled design of the jet ensures that it isn't picked up by radar.

Engine
A single Rolls-Royce Adour turbofan propels the plane to speeds above Mach 1.

Weapons
Two hidden missile bays are hidden inside the fuselage of the aircraft.

Demonstration
The Taranis will not see combat itself, but it's hoped it will inspire a fleet of similar aircraft.

Remote control
The Taranis is uncrewed, designed instead to be flown by a remote operator.

The Taranis
How this futuristic British aircraft might redefine fighter jets

KEY STATS

Length	12.4m
Wingspan	9.8m
Max range	Unknown
Top speed	Mach 1+

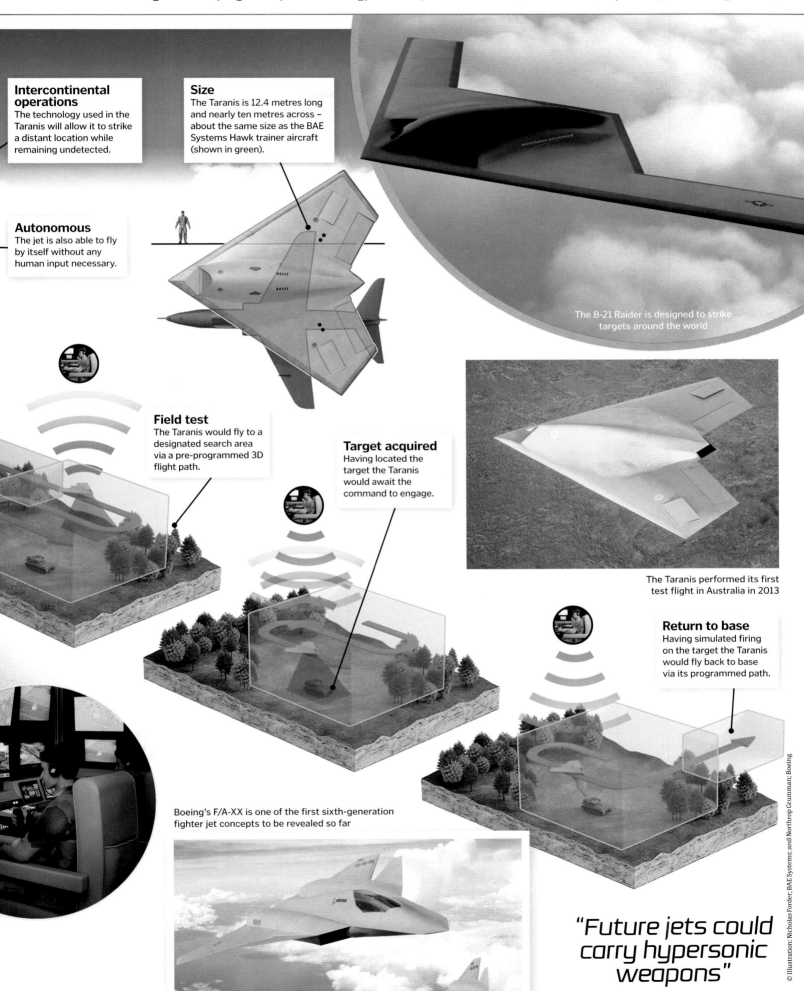

Intercontinental operations
The technology used in the Taranis will allow it to strike a distant location while remaining undetected.

Size
The Taranis is 12.4 metres long and nearly ten metres across – about the same size as the BAE Systems Hawk trainer aircraft (shown in green).

Autonomous
The jet is also able to fly by itself without any human input necessary.

The B-21 Raider is designed to strike targets around the world

Field test
The Taranis would fly to a designated search area via a pre-programmed 3D flight path.

Target acquired
Having located the target the Taranis would await the command to engage.

The Taranis performed its first test flight in Australia in 2013

Return to base
Having simulated firing on the target the Taranis would fly back to base via its programmed path.

Boeing's F/A-XX is one of the first sixth-generation fighter jet concepts to be revealed so far

"Future jets could carry hypersonic weapons"

© Illustration: Nicholas Forder; BAE Systems; 2018 Northrop Grumman; Boeing

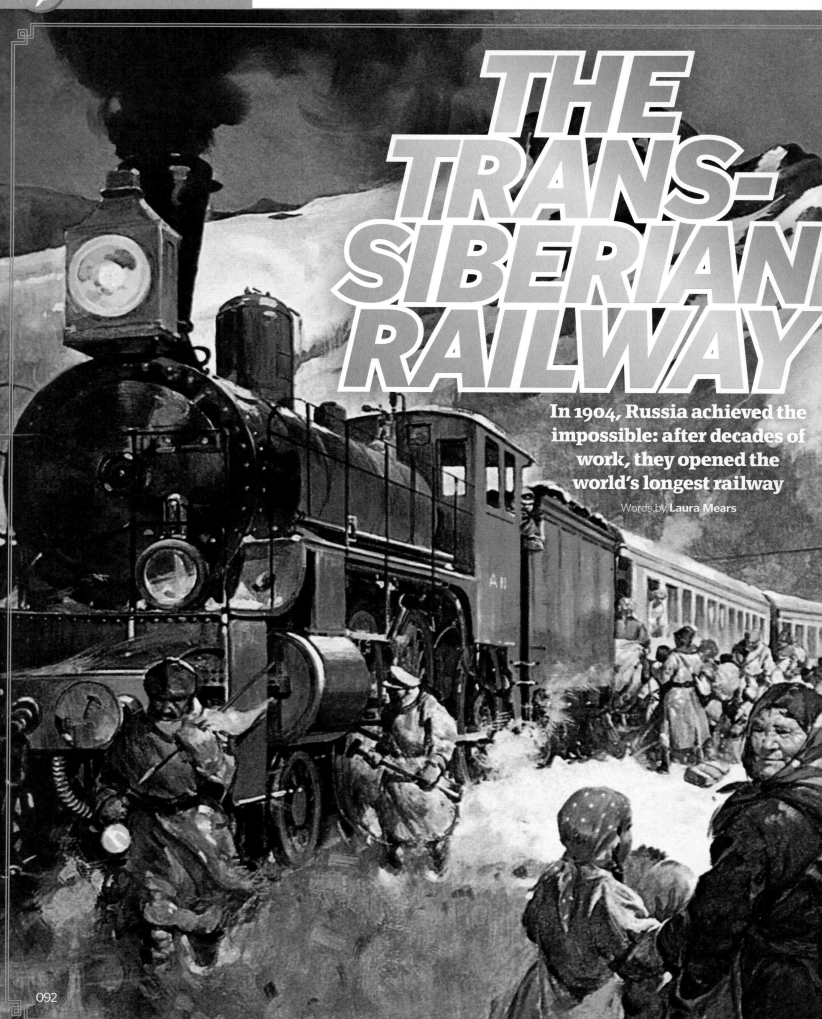

THE TRANS-SIBERIAN RAILWAY

In 1904, Russia achieved the impossible: after decades of work, they opened the world's longest railway

Words by **Laura Mears**

Built by hand through one of the harshest environments on Earth, the Trans-Siberian Railway stretches 9,258 kilometres from Moscow to Vladivostok. Hundreds of men died laying the tracks, and the project sent Russia to war with Japan, but it finally linked the West to the East.

Work on the line began when Russia was still under the rule of the Tsars. The capital of Alexander III's disjointed empire lay in the west, separated from the eastern border by desolate snow forests. The only way to cross was by wagon or along waterways that turned to ice during the winter. Russia's eastern ports froze over when the snow hit, and messages sent by telegram regularly went missing. Inside the country there was talk of revolution. Outside, Russia's eastern frontier was vulnerable to attack. They desperately needed a weatherproof transport network to unite the population.

Following in the footsteps of North America, Minister of Transport Count Sergei Witte suggested trains. A Trans-Siberian Railway could do for Siberia what the First Transcontinental Railroad did for the Wild West. However, the line would need to cover almost three times the distance. Russia didn't have America's resources – they lacked the money, the workforce and the experience. What's more, the tracks would have to pass through some of the world's roughest terrain. The railway would sit on permafrost, frozen for months at a time and liable to melt during summer. The tracks would cross rivers, travel around the world's largest freshwater lake and slice through mountains.

If they managed to pull it off, the rewards could be huge. The population in Siberia was thin and industry underdeveloped. But this inaccessible landscape, blanketed in snow for much of the year, contained most of Russia's resources. Siberia hides oil, coal, gas and diamonds. The Ural Mountains have magnetite, bauxite, gold, platinum, asbestos, talc, amethyst and topaz, and between the precious rocks there are fertile plains. Better transport links promised to make the country millions. Russia's poor would have access to new jobs. New markets would open with Japan, China and Korea, and exports could travel easily from Asia to Europe. Russia could become the gateway to the East.

Russia poured the equivalent of 50 million US dollars into the project, financing the new railway with loans and taxes. The treasury courted rich European investors, promising lavish trips to Asia. They made a deal with China, agreeing to extend the railway line into Manchuria, and they printed more money, risking the financial security of the empire.

The Tsar wanted the project finished within ten years, but the climate in Siberia made

The Soviet Union upgraded the railway, replacing the iron tracks with two strong steel lines

working during winter impossible. To save time, they planned to lay the track in six simultaneous sections. To cut costs, they would build a single iron rail instead of a double steel track, and bridges would be wood rather than metal or stone. There would be fewer sleepers to pin the track together, and they would build everything by hand – no machines or dynamite.

Gathering the men to build the track was challenging. Even with the promise of free accommodation, people were reluctant to move to Siberia from Russia's cities. Siberian natives disliked the idea of the railway and refused to work. In the end, men from China, Persia and Turkey made up much of the workforce, along with Russian prisoners and exiles. The convicts exchanged work for time off their sentences and spent their nights chained to wheelbarrows. For complicated tunnels and bridges, stonemasons

Russia drafted construction workers from China, Turkey and Persia

The railway that started a war

The Trans-Siberian Railway extended Russia's reach into the East. A deal with China took the line into Manchuria, and in return Russia secured a lease for the ice-free Chinese naval base at Port Arthur. By 1900, with construction on the main line progressing, Russia started sending troops eastwards, but not everyone welcomed their arrival. Japan also had designs on Manchuria and the Korean Peninsula. In an effort to halt Russia's unwelcome expansion, they attacked Port Arthur in 1904.

With the Siberian portions of the railway still unfinished, Russia struggled to respond. Troops became stranded at Lake Baikal, unable to cross the frozen waters. After multiple defeats, Tsar Nicholas II eventually backed down. The Treaty of Portsmouth restored peace to the region, returning Manchuria to China and giving the South Manchuria Railway to Japan.

Japan attacked during the winter with the railway at its most vulnerable

were drafted in from Italy, a nation over 6,142 kilometres away.

More than 15,000 people worked on the project, toiling from dawn until dusk, which in the high latitudes of Siberia lasted deep into the night. The men used wooden shovels, rakes and pickaxes, hefting soil and stone with their hands and relying on horses to take the heaviest loads, which were eaten when they became too weak.

Poor planning stalled the project at every turn. Engineers contracted to survey the ground failed to map every stream, river and hill, and they didn't account for the meltwater that raced over the landscape in the spring. Flooding created swamps, anthrax spread through the animals and people fell to fevers transmitted by mosquitoes. Workers eventually resorted to wearing nets to keep the insects at bay.

Together they soldiered on, crossing rivers and bogs, sometimes working waist-deep in water. They cut paths through inaccessible forests and built lines in perilous valleys. Work only stopped in winter when the weather became too harsh.

The most challenging section of track was at Lake Baikal. Bounded by mountains and coated with ice in the winter, it was all but inaccessible. The original plan was to use a boat to transport the carriages. Made in England, the Baikal Ferry had a reinforced steel hull and a propeller to cut through the ice. It was so enormous that they had to break it into chunks to get it to Siberia.

When it finally arrived, it wasn't up to the job. During the warmer months massive storms tossed the ferry off course and fog obscured the view. In the winter the ice was up to 2.7 metres thick and the propeller couldn't cut through.

Finding a way to cross the lake became urgent when Japan attacked Port Arthur in 1904, so they tried laying tracks over the ice – the first train fell straight through. They only solution was to go around, carving 38 tunnels through the granite cliffs on the shores.

As the project neared completion cost-cutting took its toll. The railway started to break before it was even finished. The complicated route and rapid construction meant that failures were common. The trains crawled slowly along the rickety lines and were often delayed, overcrowded and undersupplied. But, though broken, the railway was a triumph.

Built by hand across one of the most hostile environments in the world, it was an incredible feat of human endurance. It offered new opportunities for Russia's poor, opening a corridor to a new life. Around 5 million immigrants moved to Siberia between 1891 and 1914. In the 1950s, the Soviet Union upgraded the railway, adding a second track, steel rails, new tunnels and new bridges. Now it's one of the strongest railway lines in the world.

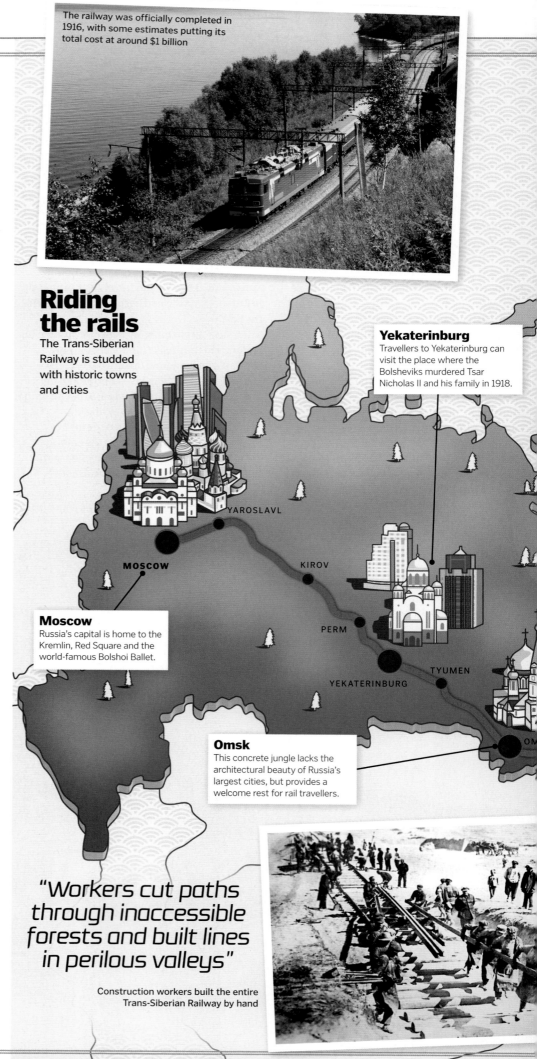

The railway was officially completed in 1916, with some estimates putting its total cost at around $1 billion

Riding the rails
The Trans-Siberian Railway is studded with historic towns and cities

Yekaterinburg
Travellers to Yekaterinburg can visit the place where the Bolsheviks murdered Tsar Nicholas II and his family in 1918.

YAROSLAVL

MOSCOW

KIROV

PERM

TYUMEN

YEKATERINBURG

Moscow
Russia's capital is home to the Kremlin, Red Square and the world-famous Bolshoi Ballet.

Omsk
This concrete jungle lacks the architectural beauty of Russia's largest cities, but provides a welcome rest for rail travellers.

OM

"Workers cut paths through inaccessible forests and built lines in perilous valleys"

Construction workers built the entire Trans-Siberian Railway by hand

An attempt to cross Lake Baikal by laying tracks over the ice ended in disaster

The Trans-Siberian Railway Network runs through one of the harshest environments on the planet

Krasnoyarsk
Home to the vast Stolby Nature Sanctuary, Krasnoyarsk is a popular stopover on the journey to Lake Baikal.

Baikal-Amur Mainline
Built on permafrost, this line provides an alternative route across northern Siberia.

Lake Baikal
This vast body of water is the oldest and deepest freshwater lake in the world.

Irkutsk
Eastern Siberia's main city, this is the place to stop if you want to visit Lake Baikal.

Trans-Mongolian
This line connects the Trans-Siberian Railway to Beijing via the Gobi Desert.

Vladivostok
This Pacific port is the final stop on the line, promising sandy beaches and beautiful architecture.

Trans-Manchurian
This historic stretch of railway passes through the Manchurian Plains of China.

RUSSIA

MONGOLIA

CHINA

KRASNOYARSK
TAYSHET
VOSIBIRSK
UST-KUT
BRATSK
SEVEROBAIKALSK
IRKUTSK
NAUSHKI
ULAN-UDE
CHITA
ZABAIKALSK
TYNDA
SKOVORODINO
BELOGORSK
KOMSOMOLSK-ON-AMUR
SOVETSKAYA GAVAN
KHABAROVSK
VLADIVOSTOK
HARBIN
CHANGCHUN
SHENYANG
ULAN BATOR
ERENHOT
DATONG
BEIJING

Lawless waters

Is it true that there are no laws in international waters?

The shipping industry is mainly regulated by the London-based International Maritime Organization (IMO)

Though you might think that international waters are a law-free zone in which it is hard to be charged for committing a crime, the high seas do in fact have legal protection and a country's jurisdiction still applies. The question is simply, which country?

It's a matter of who you are, where you are and what boat you're on. The UN Convention on the Law of the Sea (UNCLOS) outlines the classification of different bodies of water and their legal protection. In order to truly be in international waters, a vessel would need to be over 44 kilometres away from any coastline. Ships are required to sail the flag of their native country, and should a crime be committed on that boat, the laws pertaining to the nation of that flag then apply. In the absence of a flag, the law of the boat's country of registration applies. However, when a crime is committed against another vessel from another country, it can cause a battle as to who truly holds jurisdiction.

In 2012, off the coast of Kerala, India, two Italian marines were accused of the murder of two Indian fishermen. As both parties were in international waters, the men should be tried under the flag their ship was flying — Italy — but India also claimed they had legal jurisdiction and should conduct the trial. Six years on, the case has still not been tried in either country, and a decision is yet to be made.

The world's busiest station

Subway services were added to Shinjuku Station in 1959

Since its opening in 1885, Shinjuku Station has broken global records for commuter numbers

On average, 3.64 million people pass through Shinjuku Station every day, making it the world's busiest train station. Located in the southwest of central Tokyo, Shinjuku is served by five rail operators that bring people from all over the country and acts as the connection to the suburbs of Tokyo.

This transport labyrinth has 200 exits for services running from over 30 platforms and 20 tracks, and 12 train lines. The East Japan Railway Company alone serves 1.5 million people a day from the station. Despite its high volume of commuters, Japan's famous bullet trains do not pass through the station.

Busiest airport
Hartsfield-Jackson Atlanta International Airport, US

Busiest shipping lane
Dover Strait, UK

Busiest road
Ontario Highway 401, Canada

veritable Extrait de Viande LIEBIG.

LE MACADAM.

Entretien des Voies pu...

Laying a macadam road surface involved compacting the road covering with a steam road roller

The history of tarmacadam

How an accidental spillage and a sharp-eyed surveyor led to a modern road surface

In 1901, Edgar Purnell Hooley, a surveyor for Nottinghamshire County, was strolling around Denby in Derbyshire, England. As part of his role he was required to carry out odd jobs throughout the county. But on one particular day he came across an unusually smooth piece of road while passing a factory.

At the time, roads were just chipped pieces of small gravel, meaning that they quickly deteriorated as large ruts from wheels became embedded in them. The road became difficult to pass due to large amounts of dust, and sharp bits of stone able to puncture tyres. By 1820, a Scottish engineer by the name of John Loudon McAdam had created a basic road surface, but he had never found a way to stick the stones together.

The section of road Hooley was investigating looked remarkably pristine. He spoke with locals and learned that a barrel of tar had burst open across the road. In efforts to reduce the mess created by the sticky substance, a quick-thinking employee had dumped waste slag from a nearby iron works on top of the tar. This improvised resurfacing of the road had solidified and smoothed the track, inadvertently leading to the development of the modern tarmac road.

The following year, Hooley patented the process of heating tar and then mixing it with slag and broken stones. This new, hard-wearing road surface was successfully marketed as tarmacadam in honour of its original inventor. Once the recipe was perfected, Nottingham's Radcliffe Road became the first tarmac road in the world.

The first roads

The first roads were formed by humans following the game tracks created by wild animals. Over time, societies have made improvements by clearing obstacles like trees and stones from these primitive, narrow roads. As commerce increased and people moved around more to trade these trails were further improved by being flattened or widened, meaning they were able to be used to transport more human and animal traffic.

As civilisations developed and wheeled carts became more widespread, stone-paved streets were built in early cities such as those of Mesopotamia and ancient Egypt. But it was during the height of the Roman Empire that road transport really became efficient. The Romans created deep roadbeds with clay, gravel, chalk and stone allowing their armies to travel quickly between areas.

Macadam roads are still used today and feature small stones placed directly onto subsoil to make it mostly impermeable to water

ROCKET TRAVEL

Come aboard and find out why rockets are set to replace commercial aircraft

Words by **James Horton**

Anywhere in the world, in less than an hour." Elon Musk and his company SpaceX may have already revolutionised the way we utilise rocketry, but now they seek to use their technology to take us to Mars, the Moon, and even from city to city. And, quite amazingly, the price of enjoying this last application could cost the same as an economy airline ticket.

Known as the 'Big Falcon Rocket', or more simply as the BFR, SpaceX's upcoming spacecraft is set to satisfy all of our space-faring needs in one neat package. It will build upon the staggering success of their previous two rocket designs: the Falcon 9, which at the time of writing has successfully completed nine launches in 2018, and the Falcon Heavy, which first took to the skies in February of this year. These rockets have demonstrated for the first time in our history that not only can you land the first stage of a rocket booster on the ground safely, but you can reuse it. It is from this milestone that the BFR's goal to not only take people off-world, but also shuttle them around it, becomes viable and immensely promising.

Standing at a mammoth 106 metres in total, the BFR will be composed of two major stages: a 58-metre-tall booster used to lift the vehicle into orbit, and a ship mounted atop the booster. This front portion will be equipped with 1,100 tons of additional fuel and boast a large, pressurised cabin for its city-to-city launches. This will give the BFR everything it will need to send its customers into sub-orbit and speeding around the globe. Here, passengers will be treated to not only arriving at their destination ludicrously quickly, but also to the majestic views of our planet that so far only a few lucky individuals have seen. Surely those sights alone will justify the cost of the ticket, with the fast arrival time becoming a rather big cherry on top.

It should be noted that SpaceX is not alone in its lofty ambitions. Not so far away another private company, Virgin Galactic, are creeping ever closer to their own sub-orbital flights. They plan for these to initially be sold for recreation and research, but also harbour long-term goals of trans-continental transport. Unlike the BFR, their two-component system involves a jet-powered carrier aircraft and an attached rocket-powered ship, which releases from the carrier craft and launches towards space once at altitude. Across the Atlantic, UK company Reaction Engines also dream of a vehicle that can soar from the runway to space as one whole unit. Their pioneering air-breathing SABRE engine aims to be an alternative to pure rocket power or jet engine/rocket hybrids like that of Virgin Galactic. Although this technology isn't currently as tangible as SpaceX's, it would almost certainly have incredible transport applications if it were to come to fruition.

In 1873, Jules Verne published a story about a man's attempt to race around the world in 80 days. It is a tale of great adventure, but one that pales in comparison to the journey that we have taken as a species in the years since its publication. We have ascended from the ground to the air, and from the air to the realm beyond. In fact, such is the staggering progress of our technological prowess over these years that by 2023, getting around the world in 80 *minutes* may not be quite quick enough.

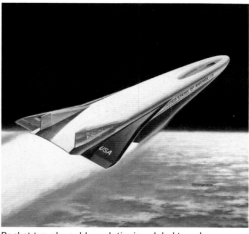
Rocket travel would revolutionise global travel by dramatically cutting down journey times

Same goal, different approach

SpaceX's plan to utilise a sub-orbital vehicle for incredibly fast transport isn't a new one. Even decades earlier in 1986, when Ronald Reagan announced his plans to fund a vehicle that could get from Washington DC, US, to Tokyo, Japan, in two hours, it wasn't a novel idea. But the difference between SpaceX's ideas and those of the past has rested in their approach to the problem.

Reagan's government and NASA wanted to construct the National Aero-Space Plane (NASP) as a single unit that could act as both aircraft and spacecraft with a unique engine design. They had shied away from rockets due to their one-use-only restriction. But the answer to finding a commercial space-faring vehicle, as SpaceX has shown, didn't lie in finding a new way to generate enough thrust to get into orbit, but in a way to make the rocket stages reusable.

Virgin Galactic's spacecraft will first be lifted to altitude by a carrier jet

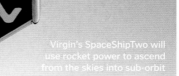
Virgin's SpaceShipTwo will use rocket power to ascend from the skies into sub-orbit

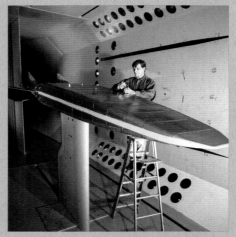
Designers anticipated that the NASP concept would travel at up to 25 times the speed of sound

Cruising
The BFR will launch at a safe distance from dense city centres, so a ship will ferry passengers to the launchpad from the mainland.

All aboard
Passengers will ascend and enter the 106m-tall vehicle. Inside, the pressurised compartment will be larger than an A380's main deck.

Cool ascent
Thanks to the engine's liquid oxygen and liquid methane fuel, the launch will feel relatively smooth and comfortable.

Smooth journey
Above our planet's dense atmosphere, passengers will be free from turbulence. They can relax and enjoy the awe-inspiring views of Earth from above.

City-to-city on the BFR

Hop aboard the Big Falcon Rocket and travel to anywhere in the world in under 60 minutes

Detachment
Its job done, the booster rocket will detach. The ship's Raptor engines will then ignite, boosting the aircraft to top speeds of 27,000kph.

Lift-off
52,700kN of thrust, provided by the booster rocket, will be used to lift the spacecraft out of the atmosphere.

Reusable
The first stage booster will be able to land autonomously. It will then be reserviced, refuelled and reused.

Journey times comparison

ROUTE	DISTANCE	FLIGHT TIME	BFR TIME
LA to New York	3,983km	5 hours, 25 min	25 min
Bangkok to Dubai	4,909km	6 hours, 25 min	27 min
Tokyo to Singapore	5,350km	7 hours, 10 min	28 min
London to New York	5,555km	7 hours, 55 min	29 min
New York to Paris	5,849km	7 hours, 40 min	30 min
Sydney to Singapore	6,288km	8 hours, 20 min	31 min
LA to London	8,781km	10 hours, 30 min	32 min
London to Hong Kong	9,648km	11 hours, 50 min	34 min
Sydney to Johannesburg	11,078km	13 hours, 35 min	37 min
Doha to Auckland	14,548km	17 hours, 43 min	45 min
Sydney to Zurich	16,576km	20 hours, 08 min	50 min
Rio de Janeiro to Hong Kong	17,709km	21 hours, 28 min	53 min

Sub-orbital transit
Unlike jet aircraft, the BFR will breach the atmosphere, continue its arc while in orbit, and make an atmospheric re-entry.

Weightlessness
After the ship's burn is complete, passengers will experience the feeling of weightlessness for a brief period as the aircraft coasts through space.

Comparable price
As the mechanical parts of BFR will be wholly reusable and its fuel incredibly cheap, passengers will pay similar prices to an economy airline ticket.

Re-entry
As the ship adjusts its orientation to slow its descent, the increased G-forces will cause passengers to feel several times heavier than usual.

Soft landing
Two engines will fire to bring the BFR to a safe and controlled stop at its destination.

"By 2023, getting around the world in 80 minutes may not be quite quick enough"

101

SPACE

104
Space
weather

110
TESS

112
The Marscopter

102

"SpaceX's Falcon Heavy is
the most powerful rocket
in operation today"

SPACE W

How radiation from the Sun and supernovae poses a constant threat to life on our planet

O ur universe can seem like a somewhat benign place, but phenomena in our Solar System and beyond can have a serious impact on life on Earth. Eruptions from the Sun and cosmic rays from afar can cause havoc with our atmosphere, affecting not just satellites and astronauts in orbit but life on Earth too. Over the years we've been getting better at predicting space weather, but the risk to Earth is ever present. So we

can never be too prepared for the next big event that heads our way.

Space weather refers to a lot of things, although it often relates mostly to the Sun, which has the most direct effect on Earth. While our star happily burns away and provides us with both light and heat, it can on occasion erupt in a violent explosion. One such event is a solar flare, when a build-up of magnetic energy is released. These normally

erupt from sunspots, which are dark and relatively cool regions on the Sun's surface. Flares are exceptionally bright, releasing large amounts of photons and other particles in our direction, and they can last from minutes to hours. They are categorised in a variety of classes, with the most powerful being X-class flares.

Another type of eruption from the Sun is a coronal mass ejection (CME). These are

EATHER

Words by **Jonny O'Callaghan**

sometimes associated with solar flares, although the exact relationship is unknown. CMEs, like solar flares, are also the result of magnetic fields building up, but they instead hurl large amounts of matter into space. They can look like large fans of gas zooming out, with the hot plasma they produce taking up to three days to reach us. Using telescopes we can see and monitor both solar flares and CMEs before they reach Earth.

The Sun can produce other space weather too. High-speed solar wind, appearing over holes in the outer atmosphere (corona) of the Sun, can head towards Earth at speeds of up to 800 kilometres per second. Solar energetic particles (SEPs), meanwhile, are high-energy particles that can be caused by both solar flares and CMEs. Carrying a large amount of energy, they can cause considerable damage if they directly hit a spacecraft.

From outside our Solar System, galactic cosmic rays (GCRs) can also be sent in our direction. These highly energetic particles constantly bombard our planet and are thought to be produced by explosive events like supernovae. When the Sun is at its most active, known as its solar maximum, it does a good job of deflecting GCRs from our planet. However, during a solar minimum every 11 years, Earth is more at risk from GCRs.

© Getty

The L5 mission

How ESA's bold proposal would help predict incoming solar weather

L1
A spacecraft at L1 sees solar weather at the same time as Earth, so it doesn't give us the same advance warning as L5.

Incoming particles
Utilising L5 could give us more accurate information on the speed of particles heading for Earth.

The Sun
As the Sun rotates, a coronal mass ejection (CME) or solar flare can come into view.

Magnetic field

L5
L5 is located about 60° behind Earth in its orbital plane around the Sun. With a side-on view, a probe positioned here can judge the speed of any solar ejections heading to Earth.

Advanced warning
A spacecraft at the L5 position would see the Sun's surface up to five days before it rotates into view of Earth.

Solar eruptions can produce stunning auroras near the poles

Ready for the storm

Early in 2018, the European Space Agency (ESA) announced it would be looking into a novel proposal to monitor space weather. While most space weather satellites are positioned in line with the Sun and Earth, this mission would be placed in a position of gravitational stability lagging behind Earth's orbit, known as Lagrange Point 5 (L5).

No mission has gone to this region before, but it offers a number of benefits. Being positioned to the 'side' of the Sun (relative to Earth), it could give us an early warning of the speed and direction of an ejection heading our way. This is because it could see the eruptions on the side of the Sun before it rotates into our view, so we'd know what was about to head our way. The ESA hopes to select a final design for the mission in mid-2019.

ESA's L5 mission will be positioned behind Earth in its orbit around the Sun

which, like SEPs, can damage spacecraft. Fortunately, thanks to our atmosphere they pose little threat to us on Earth, but astronauts travelling into space in the future may have to contend with them a bit more.

All of these space weather events can have an impact on Earth, from minor to major. The most noticeable are the auroras produced at the north and south poles as particles from a CME release other particles trapped in our planet's magnetosphere, which in turn funnel down to the poles and trigger reactions in oxygen and nitrogen molecules. The result can be a stunning light show of flashing green and purple. However, these geomagnetic storms can also affect communications with spacecraft and expose people flying in planes to more radiation. Flights are even sometimes rerouted to avoid their worst effects.

During periods of intense space weather the number of high-energy particles around Earth increases, particularly in two bands of trapped radiation that surround our planet known as the Van Allen belts. If a high-energy particle strikes a satellite in just the right way it can cause anomalies such as switching a circuit, or more seriously it can damage or knock out the satellite entirely. Sometimes satellites are put into safe mode during the strongest space weather events to protect them from the incoming radiation.

Knowing when these events will occur is therefore very important in order to allow us the time to prepare satellites to ride out the storm. Some severe events can also affect communications and power grids on Earth, which must be similarly maintained to avoid damage.

To track space weather events we have a number of spacecraft that continually monitor the Sun, each one looking for any eruptions that might send particles our way. This can give us several days' warning for the most powerful events, with the National Oceanic and Atmospheric Administration (NOAA) giving storms a rating from 1 (minor) to 5 (severe) to let people know how dangerous an incoming storm is.

Over the years we've certainly got better at monitoring space weather, but there is always the risk of an exceptionally large solar eruption in the future causing huge issues. We can mitigate most problems, but it's always better to be prepared if and when the

Major space weather events

In 1859, a solar storm known as the Carrington Event struck Earth, causing one of the largest geomagnetic storms on record. At the time it only resulted in a few telegraph pylons emitting sparks, but were the same event to happen again today the results to our infrastructure could be catastrophic.

The Carrington Event was so powerful that, by some accounts, the auroras it produced were bright enough to read a newspaper by. But it's the impact on the ground that is of most concern. The high-energy particles from such an event would ionise our upper atmosphere, sending radio communications haywire. Any associated radiation could pose a danger to astronauts in orbit, while slower-moving charged particles could cause huge disruptions, enough to bring down the electrical grid.

Fortunately, we're getting better at predicting storms like this, so hopefully if one happens again we'll be ready.

A modern Carrington Event could knock out our electric grid

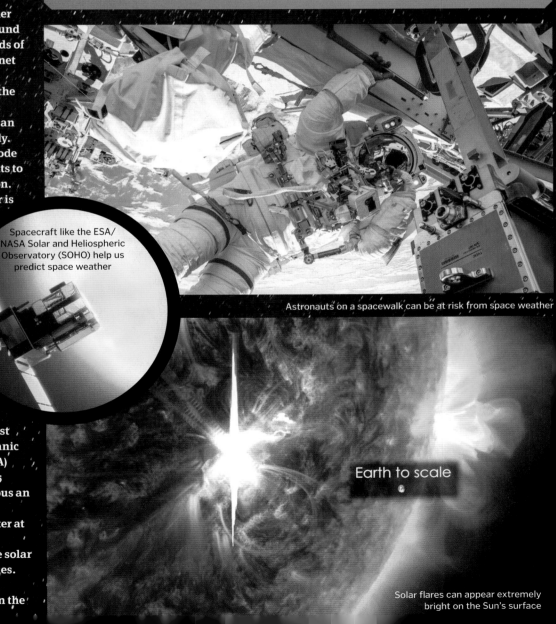
Spacecraft like the ESA/NASA Solar and Heliospheric Observatory (SOHO) help us predict space weather

Astronauts on a spacewalk can be at risk from space weather

Earth to scale

Solar flares can appear extremely bright on the Sun's surface

Cosmic rays
Radiation from distant phenomena like supernovae can pose a threat to our planet.

Impact of space weather
How space weather affects life both on Earth and in orbit

Astronaut radiation
Astronauts are exposed to more radiation than Earthlings as they are outside our planet's protective atmosphere.

Solar protons
A 'proton storm' can occur when solar particles are accelerated by the Sun's activity, reaching Earth in less than an hour.

Radiation damage
Satellites can be damaged by incoming radiation, so precautions must sometimes be taken.

Navigation errors
Severe geomagnetic storms caused by the Sun can result in errors in GPS accuracy when navigating.

In flight
Flying on a plane increases your exposure to cosmic radiation, although not by too much.

Auroras
While space weather can be dangerous, it is also the cause of wonderful auroras on our planet.

Reception
Receiving a signal from space, such as position information, can be more difficult during a space weather event.

Drilling
Geomagnetic activity caused by space weather can cause issues when directing a borehole to drill for oil or gas.

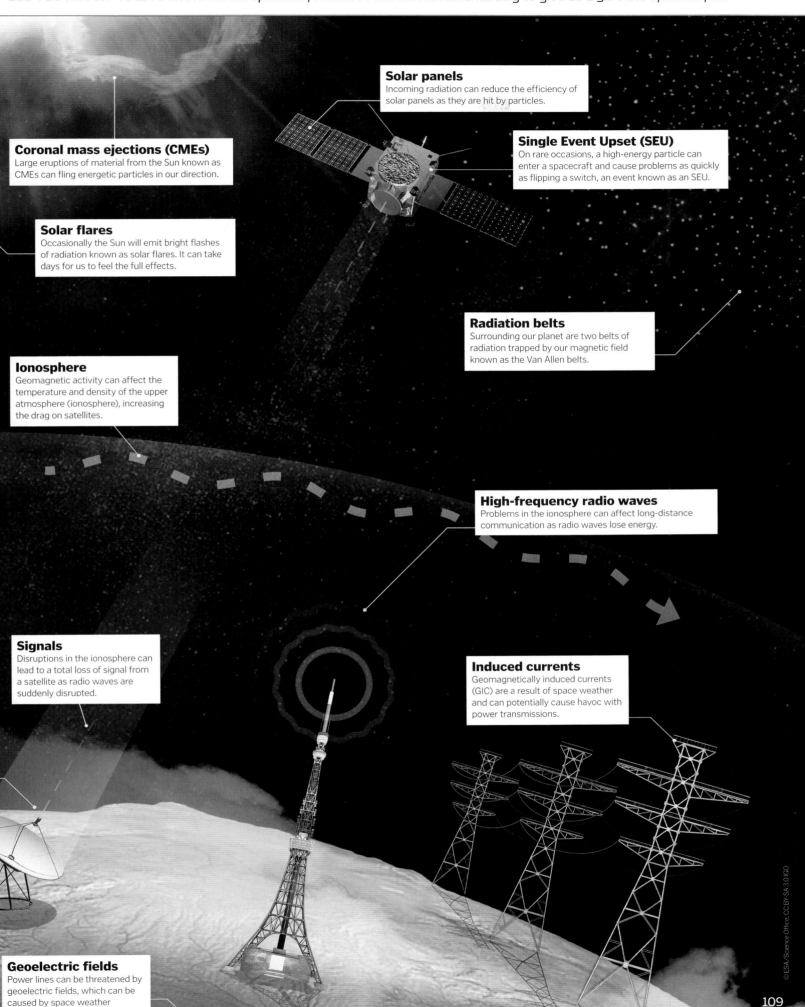

Solar panels
Incoming radiation can reduce the efficiency of solar panels as they are hit by particles.

Single Event Upset (SEU)
On rare occasions, a high-energy particle can enter a spacecraft and cause problems as quickly as flipping a switch, an event known as an SEU.

Coronal mass ejections (CMEs)
Large eruptions of material from the Sun known as CMEs can fling energetic particles in our direction.

Solar flares
Occasionally the Sun will emit bright flashes of radiation known as solar flares. It can take days for us to feel the full effects.

Radiation belts
Surrounding our planet are two belts of radiation trapped by our magnetic field known as the Van Allen belts.

Ionosphere
Geomagnetic activity can affect the temperature and density of the upper atmosphere (ionosphere), increasing the drag on satellites.

High-frequency radio waves
Problems in the ionosphere can affect long-distance communication as radio waves lose energy.

Signals
Disruptions in the ionosphere can lead to a total loss of signal from a satellite as radio waves are suddenly disrupted.

Induced currents
Geomagnetically induced currents (GIC) are a result of space weather and can potentially cause havoc with power transmissions.

Geoelectric fields
Power lines can be threatened by geoelectric fields, which can be caused by space weather

TESS

How NASA's newest planet hunter will scour the universe for other worlds

To date we have found several thousand worlds beyond our Solar System. Known as exoplanets, some of them are relatively close to Earth, while others are thousands of lightyears away. We've managed to accumulate a pretty good collection, from Earth-sized worlds to gas giants like Jupiter, mostly thanks to NASA's Kepler telescope. But we're about to find a whole lot more.

On 18 April 2018, NASA's newest planet hunter, the Transiting Exoplanet Survey Satellite (TESS), was launched on top of a SpaceX Falcon 9 rocket. Placed in an unusual orbit around Earth, this satellite will continuously peer at the night sky in an effort to find worlds orbiting stars 30-300 lightyears from us. It's hoped it may find as many as 20,000 planets, more than five times as many as we've found so far.

TESS, which measures about four metres long, will search for planets using the transit method. This involves looking at stars and noticing the dip in light as a planet passes in front of them. This technique has already been employed with great success by Kepler, but TESS will take it to a whole new level by using four cameras – rather than Kepler's single camera – to look for planets. Its primary mission will last two years, during which time it will observe 85 per cent of the sky (an area 400 times larger than Kepler).

TESS will be focusing on bright stars, with most of the planets it finds being ranging between Neptune and Earth in size. A few hundred, however, are expected to be potentially rocky places less than twice the size of Earth, and some may even be habitable. Whatever TESS finds, the next few years promise plenty of exciting discoveries.

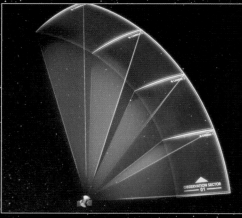

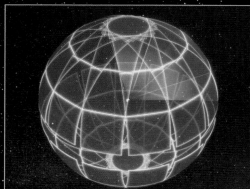

TESS will observe 85 per cent of the night sky, splitting it up into 26 segments over two years

This artist's concept depicts some of the exoplanet types TESS will be searching for

"TESS may find as many as 20,000 planets"

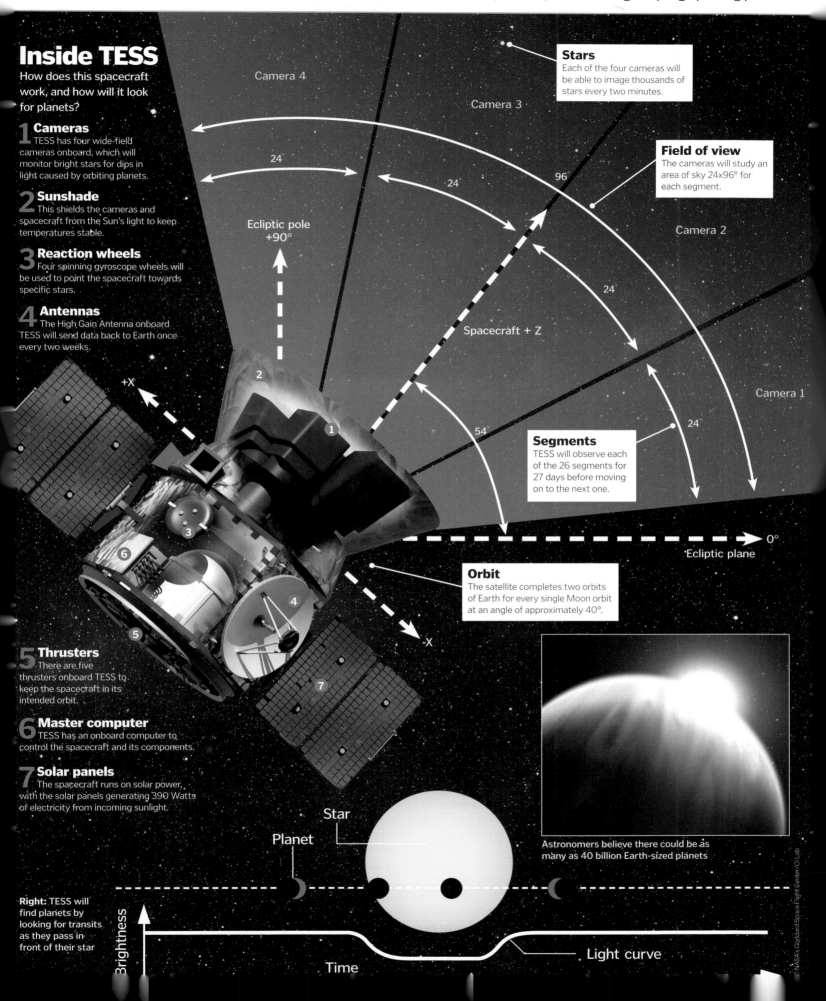

Inside TESS

How does this spacecraft work, and how will it look for planets?

1 Cameras
TESS has four wide-field cameras onboard, which will monitor bright stars for dips in light caused by orbiting planets.

2 Sunshade
This shields the cameras and spacecraft from the Sun's light to keep temperatures stable.

3 Reaction wheels
Four spinning gyroscope wheels will be used to point the spacecraft towards specific stars.

4 Antennas
The High Gain Antenna onboard TESS will send data back to Earth once every two weeks.

5 Thrusters
There are five thrusters onboard TESS to keep the spacecraft in its intended orbit.

6 Master computer
TESS has an onboard computer to control the spacecraft and its components.

7 Solar panels
The spacecraft runs on solar power, with the solar panels generating 390 Watts of electricity from incoming sunlight.

Right: TESS will find planets by looking for transits as they pass in front of their star

Camera 4

Camera 3

Stars
Each of the four cameras will be able to image thousands of stars every two minutes.

Field of view
The cameras will study an area of sky 24x96° for each segment.

Camera 2

Camera 1

24
24
96
24
54
24

Ecliptic pole +90°

Spacecraft + Z

+X

−X

0°
Ecliptic plane

Segments
TESS will observe each of the 26 segments for 27 days before moving on to the next one.

Orbit
The satellite completes two orbits of Earth for every single Moon orbit at an angle of approximately 40°.

Astronomers believe there could be as many as 40 billion Earth-sized planets

Star
Planet

Brightness
Time
Light curve

© NASA's Goddard Space Flight Center/CI Lab

The Marscopter

In a first for space exploration, NASA plan to send a flying probe to another world

In 2020, NASA will not only be launching their next rover to the Red Planet, they'll also be sending the Mars Helicopter. The autonomous flying probe will be a technology demonstration of heavier-than-air craft, possibly opening up air-based exploration missions to other planets.

Mars' atmosphere is about one per cent the density of Earth's, so achieving flight is a significant engineering challenge. To overcome this, the rotors' counter-rotating blades will spin at around 3,000rpm – almost ten-times faster than they would have to in order to fly on Earth.

If the project is successful, low-flying scouts such as this could dramatically improve the amount of ground future missions can cover. They can also support land-based rovers, providing navigational assistance by surveying possible routes and points of interest.

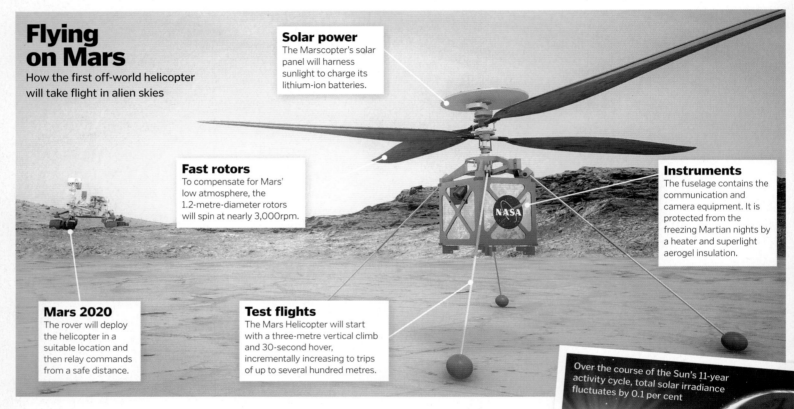

Flying on Mars

How the first off-world helicopter will take flight in alien skies

Solar power
The Marscopter's solar panel will harness sunlight to charge its lithium-ion batteries.

Fast rotors
To compensate for Mars' low atmosphere, the 1.2-metre-diameter rotors will spin at nearly 3,000rpm.

Instruments
The fuselage contains the communication and camera equipment. It is protected from the freezing Martian nights by a heater and superlight aerogel insulation.

Mars 2020
The rover will deploy the helicopter in a suitable location and then relay commands from a safe distance.

Test flights
The Mars Helicopter will start with a three-metre vertical climb and 30-second hover, incrementally increasing to trips of up to several hundred metres.

Tracking the Sun with TSIS

The latest space station sensor will help us better understand our planet's power supply

The Sun is Earth's primary energy source and the driving force behind our climate and weather systems. The amount of solar energy that reaches our planet is known as the total solar irradiance (TSI), and scientists have been measuring this continuously since 1978.

The latest device to continue these observations is the Total and Spectral Solar Irradiance Sensor (TSIS-1), installed onboard the International Space Station. This device contains two sensors that will provide the most accurate measurements of sunlight yet, monitoring the radiant energy from the Sun with the Total Irradiance Monitor (TIM) and

the distribution of that energy across different wavelengths with the Spectral Irradiance Monitor (SIM).

Our star has an 11-year cycle during which its activity naturally fluctuates. In more active times, sunspots, flares and coronal mass ejections are more common, and the Sun emits comparatively more energy than when it is less active.

TSIS-1's sensors will collect data on TSI and how the different layers of our atmosphere respond to solar energy variations. These measurements will help improve our understanding of how much of an impact the Sun's activity has on our climate.

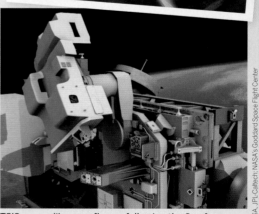

Over the course of the Sun's 11-year activity cycle, total solar irradiance fluctuates by 0.1 per cent

TSIS moves like a sunflower, following the Sun from sunrise to sunset, which is every 90 minutes on the ISS

Sleepless on the space station

Sleep is essential for our health, which is why NASA carefully studies each astronaut's sleeping patterns

Chris Hadfield points out his Drager Double Sensor, which monitors his biological clock during sleep

Many people feel that at the end of a hard day there is nothing better than collapsing onto a comfortable bed and catching some well-earned Zs when night falls. However, when you're in space it's a completely different world, and astronauts are stuck in an unusual state of perpetual weightlessness and ever-changing sunlight exposure.

For astronauts aboard the International Space Station there's no collapsing onto a bed, no falling asleep when the Sun sets, no waking up when the Sun rises, and there are constant troubles with motion sickness. This can cause problems when trying to maintain a good sleeping pattern, which refreshes and maintains the astronauts' wellbeing. This is important, as in space astronauts need to remain at maximum efficiency, and this can slip with a bad night's sleep.

This is why NASA continues to study astronauts' sleeping schedules as they plan for future space expeditions. There are many aspects that affect one's sleep, including the timing schedule, the environment, lighting and cognitive behaviour. By studying how these different details sculpt an astronaut's rest NASA can begin to plan for long-duration space travel. The journey to Mars, for example, would take roughly nine months, and sleep plays a vital part in ensuring the astronauts stay in a good state of mind and health along the way.

Astronaut Suni Williams had to wear an Actiwatch for the Sleep-Long study on the ISS

Monitoring a space slumber

Different factors contribute to a good night's sleep in space, and NASA is carefully monitoring each of these points

AIM TO SLEEP **8.5** HOURS   TEND TO SLEEP **6.0** HOURS

Sleeping periods
The aim is eight hours of sleep each 'night', but that's not normally the case. On average, crew members tend to only get between five and six hours of sleep.

Floating Cabin
Each astronaut has their own cabin. This room is where the individual can enjoy their rest in a vertical sleeping bag on the wall as opposed to a horizontal bed.

The Drager Double Sensor
These sensors monitor astronauts' core temperature and body chemistry, as well as checking for any changes to circadian rhythms, also known as the 'biological clock'.

Constant sunrises
As the space station orbits the Earth once every 90 minutes, there is no real sense of night or day. Astronauts can experience 16 sunrises and sunsets a day.

Changing light on the ISS
Lighting conditions can also impact sleep. The ISS has had its fluorescent lights replaced with solid-state LEDs, which can change colour and intensity, in order to improve sleep.

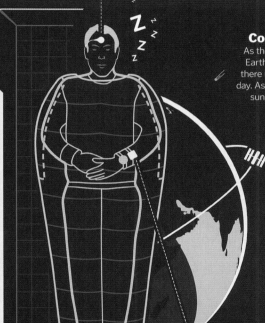

Astronaut's Actiwatch
Similar to the smartwatches we wear, these 'fitness trackers' carefully monitor an astronaut's activity while awake or asleep to see how their body is performing under microgravity.

Earth-bound implications
Insomnia can affect many people on Earth due to jet lag and working unusual shift patterns, and this can negatively affect their health. NASA hope that their ISS studies can help improve people's everyday lives.

Consequences for a Martian mission
When humans reach Mars they will need to adapt to the Martian days, which are almost 40 minutes longer than an Earth day. NASA need to study how our bodies adapt to such a situation.

©NASA

Ultraluminous X-ray sources

What causes these bright beacons to shine across the cosmos?

In our universe we keep finding strangely bright objects that fall somewhere in brightness between a star and the centre of an active galaxy. They're called ultraluminous X-ray sources (ULXs), but at the moment we're not quite sure what's causing them.

There's about one ULX per galaxy on average, each shining extremely bright with X-rays. Some of them may be intermediate-mass black holes, or even smaller black holes, blasting out energy as they suck in matter. Others are thought to be the result of neutron stars – the remnant cores of massive stars that have exploded.

Neutron stars are extraordinarily compact, containing more than the mass of our Sun squashed into a city-sized sphere. As they draw in material they heat up and emit more X-ray radiation until they reach a point called the Eddington limit, where the outgoing X-rays start pushing matter away, possibly giving rise to a ULX.

So far we've found about four ULXs that look like they're caused by neutron stars and a number of others that we think might be black holes, but the jury is still out on exactly how they work.

Ultraluminous X-ray Source

A ULX is seen here in M51, also called the Whirlpool Galaxy

Jupiter's cyclones

Recent data is giving us a whole new look at our Solar System's biggest planet

NASA's Juno spacecraft entered orbit around Jupiter in July 2016, and since then we have been treated to a feast of data and images. One of the most recent discoveries, announced in March 2018, was that Jupiter's storms were unlike anything we see on Earth.

Infrared images taken by the Juno spacecraft, like the example below, have shown that each pole of Jupiter has a fascinating polygonal pattern of cyclones, with winds reaching speeds of up to 350 kilometres per hour. At the north pole a central cyclone is surrounded by eight more that measure up to 4,600 kilometres across. At the south pole there are just five surrounding cyclones, but they measure up to 7,000 kilometres across. The cyclones at both poles are so densely packed together

that they are almost touching each other, but they're still able to maintain their individual shapes.

Juno is the first mission that's been designed to fly over Jupiter's poles, so it's the first chance we're really getting to have a good look at them. And how weird they're turning out to be.

Thanks to Juno, we have gained new insights into Jupiter's storms

Jupiter's south pole, as seen by Juno's Jovian Infrared Auroral Mapper (JIRAM)

An update on the TRAPPIST-1 system

What have we recently discovered about this intriguing exoplanet system?

An artist's impression of TRAPPIST-1's seven planets, three of which may be habitable

Since the record-breaking discovery of its seven Earth-sized planets was announced in February 2017, the TRAPPIST-1 system has stirred excitement and curiosity among the scientific community. Located almost 40 lightyears away from us, the exoplanet system's rocky planets orbit a cool, red dwarf sun. To make things even more interesting, three of the planets (TRAPPIST-1e, f and g) are located within the star's habitable zone, a region where temperatures are suitable for liquid water to exist. The system's age has recently been narrowed down to between 9.8–5.4 billion years, meaning that it may be twice as old as our own Solar System.

In May 2016, researchers using The Transiting Planets and Planetesimals Small Telescope (TRAPPIST) in Chile announced the discovery of three planets in the system. After follow-up observations using the Spitzer Space Telescope and other ground-based observatories, a total of seven roughly Earth-sized worlds were revealed.

This spark of scientific curiosity has continued to reveal new gems of information, and other observatories continue to collect further data. When Hubble recently examined the atmospheres of TRAPPIST-1d, e and f, the only thing it could decipher was a lack of hydrogen. This is a positive sign, as it means that there could be higher concentrations of heavier elements like those in Earth's atmosphere, making for a more exciting prospect of habitability.

Red dwarfs are the most common star types in the galaxy, so this potentially habitable system around TRAPPIST-1 is a promising discovery in our hunt for alien life.

Jupiter & Major Moons

Io Europa Ganymede Callisto

Galilean moon equivalent
TRAPPIST-1b orbits closer to its host star than the most distant Galilean moon, Callisto, around Jupiter.

Tidal heating
Due to the close proximity of the TRAPPIST-1 exoplanets it's thought they all experience tidal heating, similar to the Galilean moons.

TRAPPIST-1 vs the Solar System

These curious differences between our Solar System and TRAPPIST-1 make for a tantalising target

TRAPPIST-1 System

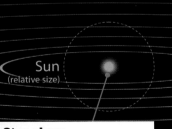

Sun
(relative size)

b   c   d   e   f   g   h

Closer than Mercury
TRAPPIST-1h, the most distant TRAPPIST-1 exoplanet, orbits its host star at roughly 16 per cent the distance of Mercury around the Sun.

Star sizes
The host star, TRAPPIST-1, is an ultracool red dwarf star with only 8.9 per cent the mass of our Sun.

Atmosphere analysis
TRAPPIST-1d, e and f appear to have a lack of hydrogen in their atmospheres, which is a positive sign for having Earth-like conditions.

Orbits Enlarged 25x

Inner Solar System

Earth-sized exoplanets
All TRAPPIST-1 exoplanets are roughly Earth sized, ranging from just 23 per cent smaller to 15 per cen larger than our home plan

Mercury   Venus   Earth   Mars

Hotting up
The highest equilibrium temperature within the system is that of TRAPPIST-1b, at 119°C. This is much cooler than the hottest planet in our own Solar System, Venus, which is around 470°C on average.

How to build the ULTIMATE ROCKET

The megarockets that could launch missions to the Moon, Mars and beyond

Words by **Jonathan O'Callaghan**

NASA tests a model of its SLS rocket in a wind tunnel

The SLS's liquid hydrogen tank (right) is nearly 40m tall

NASA's Saturn V rocket consumed around 20tn of fuel per second

Rockets come in a variety of sizes, from the relatively small to the monstrously big. It's those bigger rockets, however, known as heavy-lift rockets, that really stir up some major excitement. Just recently we were treated to the launch of SpaceX's huge new Falcon Heavy rocket, the most powerful rocket in operation today. But we've had bigger rockets before, and in the near future we'll have even more powerful megarockets that will put their predecessors to shame.

Building a rocket is no mean feat. Essentially, you've got one or more powerful jet engines strapped to a tall, narrow structure. That engine has to get your rocket moving fast enough to escape the pull of Earth's gravity. While some rockets are more powerful than others, they all work under the same basic principles. In order to send something into space, you not only need to fight against Earth's gravity, but you also need to be going fast enough to enter orbit.

Consider throwing a ball forwards – the faster you throw it, the further it will go, but it'll always come back to Earth. If you were some sort of superhuman, however, and could throw it hard enough, then you could theoretically make it go all the way around Earth and hit you in the back of the head.

It's the same idea with rockets. On the smaller scale you've got sounding rockets, which can take cargo weighing up to a few hundred kilograms on short 'hops' into space. They have small engines capable of thrust of more than 450 kilograms of force, which is not enough to reach orbit. Even so, they can send their cargo beyond the Karman Line – the official line of space 100 kilometres up – for minutes or hours. As you move up the rocket sizes, you move up in thrust as well as size. The more thrust a rocket has, the further it can go. If your rocket is powerful enough, you'll be able to send cargo, or even people, into Earth orbit. From there, you can use a smaller engine to then leave Earth's orbit. This is how we've sent spacecraft to the Moon and beyond.

At the upper end of the scale you'll find SpaceX's heavy-lift rocket, the Falcon Heavy, which has 2.3 million kilograms-force of thrust. It launched for the first time on

"SpaceX's Falcon Heavy is the most powerful rocket in operation today

Saturn V

NASA's Saturn V rocket was developed in response to the Soviet Union placing the first human in space, Yuri Gagarin, in 1961. The rocket's purpose was to launch astronauts to the Moon, which it did successfully on six occasions. But to do that, the rocket needed to be big, and it needed to be powerful. So NASA went about building the biggest rocket the world had ever seen, towering 110.6 metres high. With a thrust of over 3.4 million kilograms-force, it was capable of launching all the components of the Apollo mission in a single launch. This made it the world's first ultra rocket. So far it remains unbeaten and the holder of the accolade of most powerful rocket ever

6 February 2018 to global acclaim, and it's capable of taking 63,800 kilograms of cargo into low-Earth orbit. It's not the most powerful rocket ever launched though. That honour belongs to NASA's Saturn V rocket, which was launched 13 times in the 1960s and 1970s. With an incredible 3.4 million kilograms-force of thrust and towering some 111 metres tall, it was capable of taking 140,000 kilograms into orbit. NASA is also developing a new heavy-lift rocket called the Space Launch System (SLS), which will have 4.2 million kilograms-force of thrust. It's expected to fly in 2020 at the earliest.

Heavy-lift rockets are important as they enable the launch of bigger and better spacecraft to a greater distance. The more thrust there is, the more fuel that can be taken into orbit, and thus the further and faster the rocket can go. While smaller rockets have been used to travel to destinations like Mars, Saturn and even as far out as the dwarf planet Pluto, these bigger rockets mean a reduction in the time taken to travel there and an increase in the amount of equipment that can be transport. NASA's Saturn V rocket, for example, enabled a whole

spacecraft, lunar lander and lunar ascent vehicle to be taken with humans to the Moon in a single flight.

All rockets rely on using either liquid fuel or solid fuel. The former uses fuel like kerosene, along with an oxidiser – normally liquid oxygen. Using this set up you can control the flow of fuel to the engine, allowing you to turn the engine off and on. This is particularly useful if, say, you want to try and land your rocket boosters on the ground – as SpaceX has been doing for the last few years. Solid fuel, meanwhile, uses fuel and an oxidiser that is pre-mixed. Like a firework, once it's ignited you can't turn it off, but it's useful because it's simpler, safer and cheaper. Solid rocket boosters were used alongside a liquid-fuel rocket on the Space Shuttle to give it an extra kick to reach orbit, and they'll be used on the SLS.

The SLS will have two solid rocket boosters on the side and will not be reusable

SpaceX's Falcon Heavy, on the other hand, uses three liquid-fuelled rocket boosters. The reason is so that SpaceX can restart the rockets on their way back to Earth, allowing them to touch down back on the ground or a drone ship, as they have done with their Falcon 9 rockets. On their maiden Falcon Heavy launch, two of these boosters touched down simultaneously in a stunning event, while the third unfortunately just missed its landing on a ship. By reusing these boosters, SpaceX hopes to dramatically undercut its competitors on price. The Falcon Heavy costs just $90 million to launch, while its nearest competitor, the Delta IV Heavy, is at least four times that – and half as powerful.

"Heavy-lift rockets enable the launch of bigger and better spacecraft"

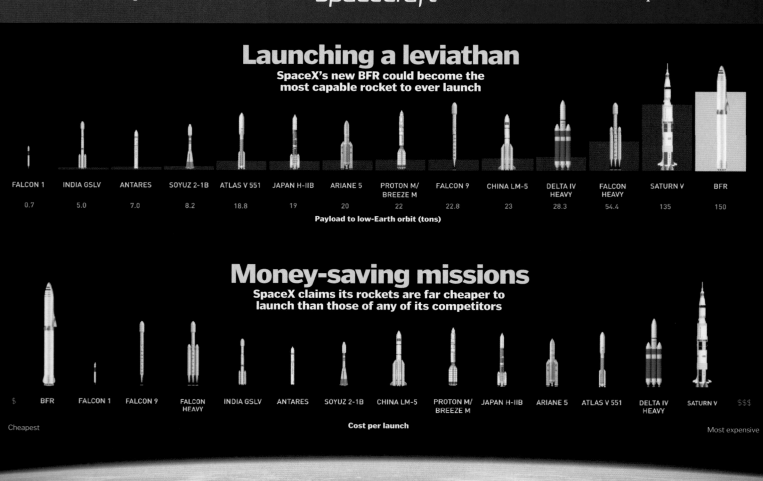

Launching a leviathan
SpaceX's new BFR could become the most capable rocket to ever launch

FALCON 1	INDIA GSLV	ANTARES	SOYUZ 2-1B	ATLAS V 551	JAPAN H-IIB	ARIANE 5	PROTON M/ BREEZE M	FALCON 9	CHINA LM-5	DELTA IV HEAVY	FALCON HEAVY	SATURN V	BFR
0.7	5.0	7.0	8.2	18.8	19	20	22	22.8	23	28.3	54.4	135	150

Payload to low-Earth orbit (tons)

Money-saving missions
SpaceX claims its rockets are far cheaper to launch than those of any of its competitors

$ BFR | FALCON 1 | FALCON 9 | FALCON HEAVY | INDIA GSLV | ANTARES | SOYUZ 2-1B | CHINA LM-5 | PROTON M/ BREEZE M | JAPAN H-IIB | ARIANE 5 | ATLAS V 551 | DELTA IV HEAVY | SATURN V | $$$

Cost per launch

Cheapest

Most expensive

SpaceX had originally planned to use its Falcon Heavy rocket to launch humans, but they're now already working on their next project – the bigger and better Big Falcon Rocket (BFR). First teased by CEO Elon Musk in 2016, this huge rocket is intended to one day enable us to colonise Mars by launching about 100 people at a time. Towering 106 metres tall, it will be capable of taking 150,000 kilograms into orbit (more than the Saturn V), with a reusable spaceship on top of a large booster below. The company wants to start launching it in 2020, although some are sceptical of SpaceX's bold claims.

NASA's SLS, in comparison, is intended to launch smaller spacecraft with crews of six people or so. NASA wants to use this rocket to build a new space station in lunar orbit, send humans to the Moon and possibly one day send humans to Mars. With an upper limit of just 130,000 kilograms to orbit, however, and with no plans to make the rocket reusable, many are questioning why NASA is building it – at a cost of $2.6 billion (around £1.9 billion) a year – when SpaceX appears to be making such great strides. Whether the SLS actually sees the light of day remains to be seen. But with a first launch touted for 2020, if it does get built, it might look rather paltry compared to the BFR.

One thing that's for sure though is we're likely to see some new rocket tests in the near future. Typically, when a rocket is tested for the first time, it includes some sort of test mass – like a block of concrete – although it often includes something of scientific value as well, like a student-led experiment. Elon Musk chose not to follow this tradition on the inaugural launch of the Falcon Heavy rocket, instead sending his own Tesla Roadster car into space on a journey that will take it out to the orbital path of Mars and back again. It will likely remain on this path for millions of years until it eventually hits another body.

The first flight of the SLS will send an unmanned NASA spacecraft, the Orion vehicle, on a journey around the Moon. We're also expecting to see another heavy-lift rocket, Jeff Bezos' Blue Origin's New Glenn rocket, launch in the next few years.

These new megarockets provide us with a range of new capabilities. Able to take bigger objects into orbit in larger quantities, they could enable some rather grandiose missions. Already the Falcon Heavy has sent waves through the launch industry with its low cost. Whether SpaceX can continue making headway, and what impact NASA's SLS will have, will be revealed in due course, but the next few years will certainly be exciting.

A brief history of SpaceX

How Elon Musk's company went from start-up to stardom in less than two decades

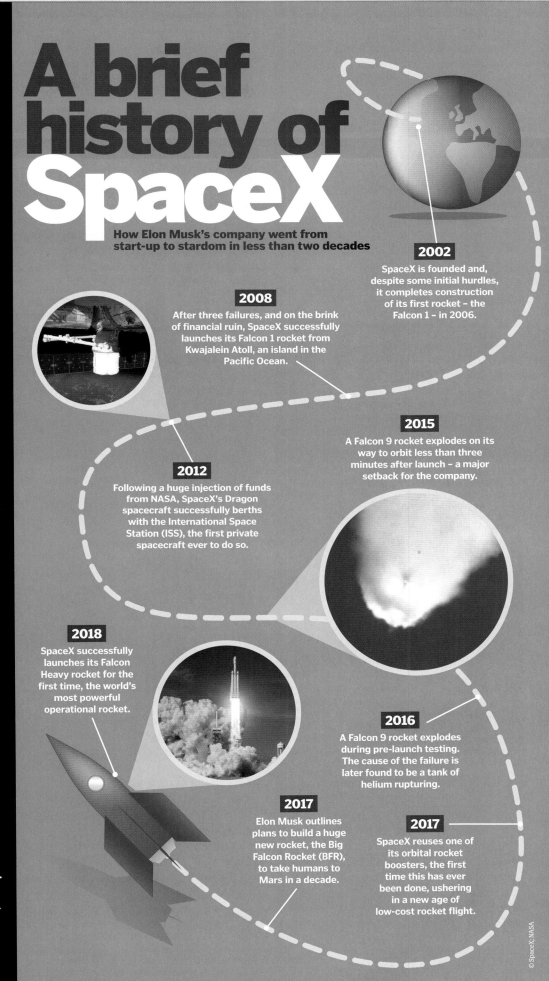

2002
SpaceX is founded and, despite some initial hurdles, it completes construction of its first rocket – the Falcon 1 – in 2006.

2008
After three failures, and on the brink of financial ruin, SpaceX successfully launches its Falcon 1 rocket from Kwajalein Atoll, an island in the Pacific Ocean.

2015
A Falcon 9 rocket explodes on its way to orbit less than three minutes after launch – a major setback for the company.

2012
Following a huge injection of funds from NASA, SpaceX's Dragon spacecraft successfully berths with the International Space Station (ISS), the first private spacecraft ever to do so.

2018
SpaceX successfully launches its Falcon Heavy rocket for the first time, the world's most powerful operational rocket.

2016
A Falcon 9 rocket explodes during pre-launch testing. The cause of the failure is later found to be a tank of helium rupturing.

2017
Elon Musk outlines plans to build a huge new rocket, the Big Falcon Rocket (BFR), to take humans to Mars in a decade.

2017
SpaceX reuses one of its orbital rocket boosters, the first time this has ever been done, ushering in a new age of low-cost rocket flight.

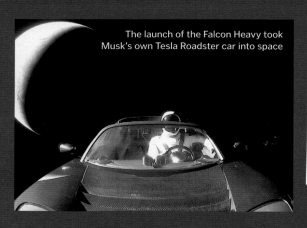

The launch of the Falcon Heavy took Musk's own Tesla Roadster car into space

The Falcon Heavy's inaugural launch saw two boosters land simultaneously

FALCON HEAVY

Inside the SpaceX behemoth that wowed audiences in February 2018

Second stage
The second stage of the rocket has a single Merlin 1D engine to take the spacecraft on the rest of its journey after detaching from the boosters.

Size
The Falcon Heavy is 70m, 12.2m wide and has a mass of over 1.4mn kg.

Reusable
All three of the main boosters on the Falcon Heavy are reusable, capable of landing on the ground or on floating drone ships.

27 engines
The Falcon Heavy uses 27 Merlin 1D engines at its base to achieve its immense thrust, using a mix of kerosene and liquid oxygen as fuel.

31 engines
The BFR will have 31 of SpaceX's new Raptor engines to produce enough thrust to lift 150,000kg into orbit, more than the Saturn V.

"The Falcon Heavy has sent waves through the launch industry"

Spaceship
The second part of the rocket is the reusable spaceship, which will apparently be capable of launching 100 people. It's 48m tall and 9m wide.

Payload fairing
The case around the nose cone, known as the payload fairing, detaches in space. SpaceX have been attempting to reuse this too in efforts to further bring down the cost of a launch.

Deep space destinations
The entire system is designed to be reusable, and Elon Musk envisages the BFR being used for trips to Mars and beyond. Ultimately, he wants to colonise Mars using the BFR.

Fuel
The BFR will use supercooled liquid methane and oxygen to power its engines. It will have a thrust of 5.4mn kg of force.

Booster
The huge single main bottom booster of the BFR, called the BRB, measures 58m tall. The whole thing will be reusable.

PROS AND CONS OF REUSABLE ROCKETS

1 They're really cheap
Being able to reuse a rocket means the cost of launching can be greatly reduced by ten times or more, as the only costs are fuel.

2 Refurbishment is a pain
Reusable rockets must be refurbished after each launch, although the costs of doing so are still much less than building a new rocket.

3 More launches
If the turnaround time on each rocket can be lessened, then the number of rockets that can be launched can be increased substantially.

4 Testing, testing, testing
As the rockets are used over and over again, they can be tested repeatedly and modified to sort out any minor problems, rather than engineers having to start from scratch with a whole new rocket.

5 Less waste
Discarding rockets in the oceans or on land, as is often done on expendable launches, has been likened to throwing away an aircraft after every single flight.

6 Wear and tear
Reusable rockets must be thoroughly checked and tested after each landing to make sure they are still safe to fly again.

The BFR plays a major role in Musk's Mars colony plans

The BFR could be used for satellite launches, ISS missions, journeys to the Moon and beyond

How SpaceX's huge proposed rocket will take humans to Mars
BIG FALCON ROCKET (BFR)

ENVIRONMENT

124
It's morphing time

132
What makes a
wave break?

130
Wildflower
meadows

134
Super volcanoes

"Currently, there is nothing we can do to stop a supervolcano"

133
The world's largest waterfall

IT'S
MORPHING
TIME

Discover the transformative power of metamorphosis
and the range of species that undergo it

Words by **Scott Dutfield**

As children we are taught the simple transformations of some species; the iconic blossoming of a butterfly and the tail-shedding cycle of tadpoles, for example. Known as metamorphosis, this process completely changes an animal's anatomy. However, this transformation is far from simple and spreads across a wide range of species.

At first glance, it's easy to come to the conclusion that a caterpillar and butterfly could be identified as two completely different species. English physician William Harvey did just that in 1651, describing metamorphosis as a process whereby free-living embryos had escaped eggs, which provided little nutritional value. He also suggested that what we now know is the pupa stage was in fact a second egg from which a new species was reborn. Dutch biologist Jan Swammerdam later discredited Harvey's theory in 1669 when he realised that the larva, pupa and adult stages all belonged to a single species.

There are two different types of metamorphosis: complete and incomplete. The differences between the two isn't whether or not a tadpole becomes a complete frog versus one that still has its tail; it relates to the species' level of anatomical change.

Complete metamorphosis occurs in those that completely change their physical characteristics, for example, a caterpillar changing into butterfly. On the other hand, incomplete metamorphosis results in only some changes, such as those seen in crickets, where the larval stage doesn't involve the development of wings but otherwise does look similar to its adult counterpart.

SHEDDING SKIN FOR WINGS

Insects are the most diverse class of animals on the planet, made even more diverse if you consider their change in forms, an occurrence that some undergo more than once in their lives. Some species start out in water as aquatic larvae, such as dragonflies, while others munch their way through vegetation on land. Many stay in their infant environment, but others decide to ditch walking or swimming and take to the skies. So how do insects shed their skin for wings?

Insect larvae carry a cellular bag of tricks within their bodies in order to carry out complete metamorphosis. Known as imaginal discs, these sac-like epithelial structures are

> "Metamorphosis is far from simple and spreads across a wide range of species"

the driving force for insect transformation. Once a caterpillar or ladybird larva has finished a series of moulting (where it has shed its skin multiple times) it enters the pupa stage in a chrysalis. While snuggled up in its new home, digestive enzymes break down part the of larva's cellular structure with the exception of the imaginal discs. This creates a kind of chunky insect soup, with the imaginal discs playing the role of pieces of diced vegetables. During this process the discs begin to form the external structures of the soon-to-be butterfly. Working from the outside in, these structures will continue to form organs, wing veins and eyes.

Incomplete metamorphosis doesn't involve such an intense transformation. Crickets start out as nymphs rather than larvae, and instead of becoming a pupa they undergo several series of moulting, a process known as ecdysis. A nymph's exoskeleton will become too tight and, prompted by the juvenile hormone ecdysone, the nymph will form new skin and step out of the old one. The wings also develop at this stage, after which the nymph grows to its adult size.

TRADING TAILS FOR LEGS

The defining feature of amphibians is their ability to live both in water and on land, and much like insects, many amphibious species start out their lives in the water. However, unlike insects, when amphibians undergo the process of complete metamorphosis, there is a distinct lack of a chrysalis or cocoon to shelter a metamorphic soup.

In order to trade their tails for legs, most amphibians rely upon hormones to trigger the chain reaction of limb loss and limb growth while still swimming around. Thyroid hormones (TH) and prolactin hormones (PRL) are the predominant biological chemicals that control the process of metamorphosis. The two work together in a balancing act. TH is the agent of change and ultimately causes the gene expression that results in a frog's transformation, while PRL works as a blocker to TH. As a frog begins its life as a tadpole, the ratio of TH and PRL levels are low. As they move through the stages of metamorphosis, PRL levels will decrease as TH levels increase, allowing the frog's anatomy to change over time. This accumulation of chemicals results in amphibians making the necessary internal changes needed to survive for life on dry land.

Gills that formed in the larval/tadpole stages are now slowly absorbed and replaced with lungs. The intestinal structures in a larva are much longer than those of its future form; during metamorphosis this length is shortened. Larvae

Newt and salamander larvae present extending gills, which restrict and develop into lungs during metamorphosis

Dragonflies undergo incomplete metamorphosis; their marine-dwelling larvae have a similar anatomy as their adult forms

> "The transformation process creates a kind of chunky insect soup"

Inside a chrysalis

A study in the Journal of the Royal Society Interface used X-ray computed tomography (CT scans) to create a 3D model of the stages of metamorphic development within a chrysalis. This technique is used in hospitals to scan human organs for damage.

Over 16 days, nine individual chrysalises were scanned at different stages of development. The scans revealed the visual internal growth of a butterfly's complex respiratory system, wing veins and creation of a waste system, known as Malpighian tubules. The gut of the larvae also becomes visibly shorter during the process of metamorphosis.

The study not only exposed the internal workings of insect transformations; the technique used will also enable us to study the effects of toxic chemicals on insect species and their development.

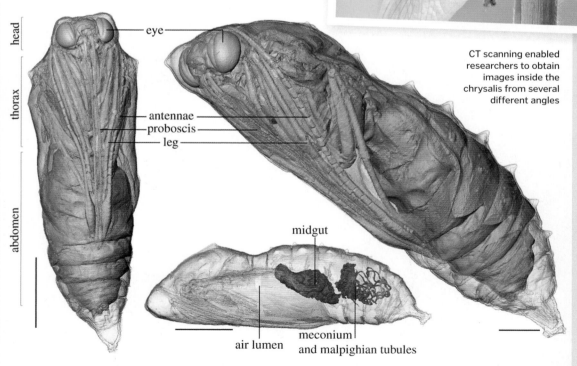

CT scanning enabled researchers to obtain images inside the chrysalis from several different angles

head

thorax

abdomen

eye

antennae
proboscis
leg

midgut

air lumen

meconium and malpighian tubules

Frog metamorphosis
What changes have to be made in order to turn a tadpole into a frog?

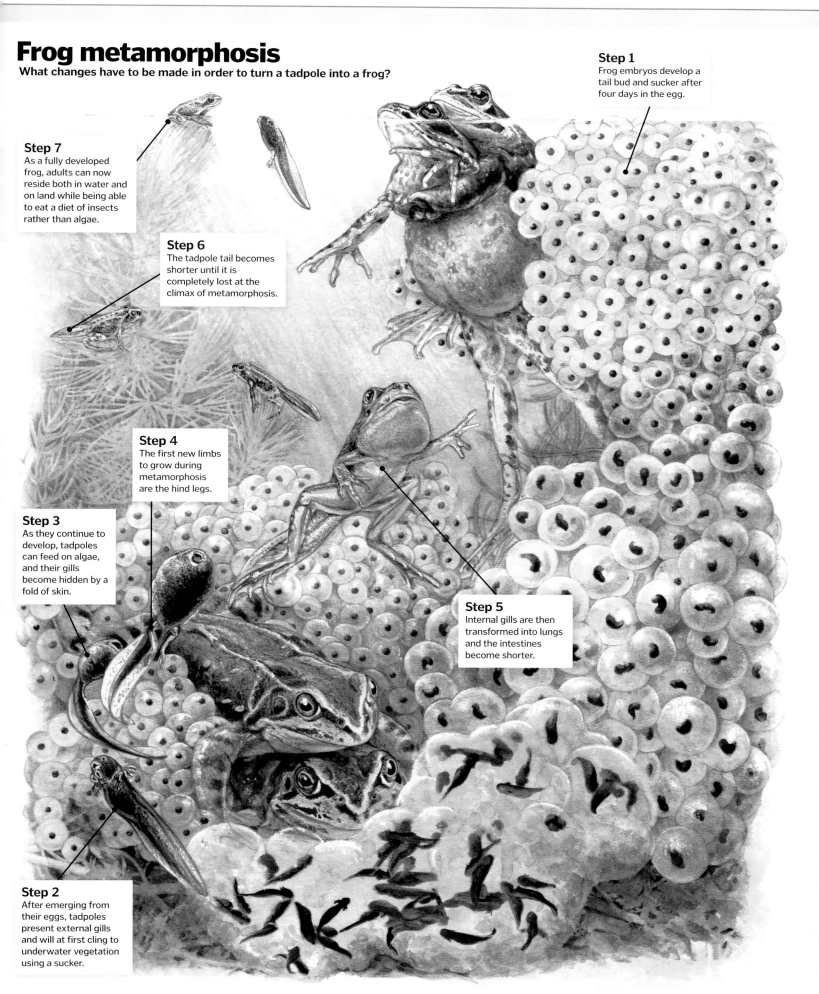

Step 1
Frog embryos develop a tail bud and sucker after four days in the egg.

Step 7
As a fully developed frog, adults can now reside both in water and on land while being able to eat a diet of insects rather than algae.

Step 6
The tadpole tail becomes shorter until it is completely lost at the climax of metamorphosis.

Step 4
The first new limbs to grow during metamorphosis are the hind legs.

Step 3
As they continue to develop, tadpoles can feed on algae, and their gills become hidden by a fold of skin.

Step 5
Internal gills are then transformed into lungs and the intestines become shorter.

Step 2
After emerging from their eggs, tadpoles present external gills and will at first cling to underwater vegetation using a sucker.

127

feed on plant matter, which takes longer to digest than the insects that adults eat, therefore the intestines are longer in tadpoles than in adult frogs. The same is true in other amphibian species, such as newts and salamanders.

Studies have revealed that there are other forces that can trigger these biological transformations, in particular environmental ones. Ponds naturally dry up as the seasons change, and as this natural process begins it acts like an eviction notice for the salamander larvae, for example. In artificial recreations of these conditions, scientists found that as the oxygen and water levels of a dying pond decreased, larvae were prompted to hurry up and grow some legs and lungs, and sure enough they did.

TRANSFORMING BELOW THE TIDES

Metamorphosis isn't just seen in the bugs and frogs of the world but in many marine creatures too. Jellyfish undergo the process of biological transformation, similar to metamorphosis in insects. They begin their lives as a stalk-like polyp. Attached to the seafloor, over time the polyp will break down into segments and form tiny jellyfish in a process called strobilation. These baby jellyfish (ephyrae) will gradually grow into adults (medusa). In one particular species, known as

the immortal jellyfish, this process can be reversed, allowing adults to revert back to their juvenile stage, essentially giving them ever-lasting life.

Another terrific marine transformer is the sea slug (nudibranch). Not only weird and wonderful in both their vibrant colour and odd physical forms, their microscopic transformations to become adults are also awe-inspiring.

Beginning life as tiny organisms called veligers, these mini sea slugs reside in their own microscopic shells, which they shed during metamorphosis and after eating a lot of plankton. In order for these sea slugs to develop into the oddities of the seafloor, their internal and external physicalities are both transformed.

CHANGING FOR SURVIVAL

It's clear that these animal transformers have a fascinating lifecycle, but why do they feel the need to change it all? Fossil records for insect metamorphosis date back 280–300 million years, and it's suggested that complete metamorphosis evolved from incomplete metamorphosis over time. The predominant theory as to why these transformations occurred in the first place was due to the need to reduce competition.

It has been proposed that creatures that could change form did so to ensure their survival when competing for resources. A tadpole or dragonfly larva will take its food from the water, whereas their future selves get their food from above the surface. Having offspring that live in a different environment, or demand different resources, eliminates the competition between juveniles and adults, thus extending the chances of survival for both.

> *"Creatures that could change form did so to ensure their survival"*

Nudibranches start life as microscopic-sized larvae that resemble a tiny sea snail before transforming into their adult forms

Far from the bright red body of their adult forms, ladybird larvae metamorphosise in a similar way to butterflies

Step 8
Adult monarch butterflies will go on to live another two to six weeks in the summer. Those born later in the year will migrate to warmer climes and live for around six to nine months.

Step 7
Adults break through their chrysalis and unfold their newly acquired wings and transformed body. The butterflies have now completed their transformation and will not grow any bigger.

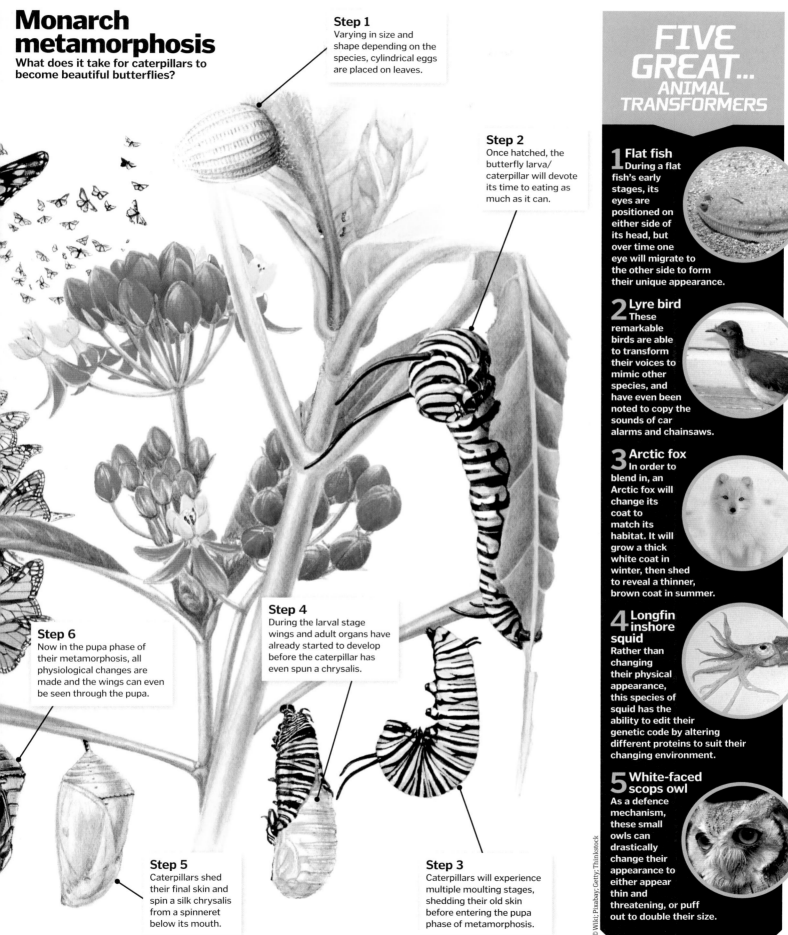

Monarch metamorphosis

What does it take for caterpillars to become beautiful butterflies?

Step 1
Varying in size and shape depending on the species, cylindrical eggs are placed on leaves.

Step 2
Once hatched, the butterfly larva/caterpillar will devote its time to eating as much as it can.

Step 4
During the larval stage wings and adult organs have already started to develop before the caterpillar has even spun a chrysalis.

Step 6
Now in the pupa phase of their metamorphosis, all physiological changes are made and the wings can even be seen through the pupa.

Step 5
Caterpillars shed their final skin and spin a silk chrysalis from a spinneret below its mouth.

Step 3
Caterpillars will experience multiple moulting stages, shedding their old skin before entering the pupa phase of metamorphosis.

FIVE GREAT... ANIMAL TRANSFORMERS

1 Flat fish
During a flat fish's early stages, its eyes are positioned on either side of its head, but over time one eye will migrate to the other side to form their unique appearance.

2 Lyre bird
These remarkable birds are able to transform their voices to mimic other species, and have even been noted to copy the sounds of car alarms and chainsaws.

3 Arctic fox
In order to blend in, an Arctic fox will change its coat to match its habitat. It will grow a thick white coat in winter, then shed to reveal a thinner, brown coat in summer.

4 Longfin inshore squid
Rather than changing their physical appearance, this species of squid has the ability to edit their genetic code by altering different proteins to suit their changing environment.

5 White-faced scops owl
As a defence mechanism, these small owls can drastically change their appearance to either appear thin and threatening, or puff out to double their size.

© Wiki; Pixabay; Getty; Thinkstock

Wildflower meadows

Discover the wild side of meadows and how you can make your own

Wildflower meadows, though vibrant and beautiful, play a vital role in maintaining pollinator populations, increasing biodiversity and providing habitats.

Whether it's the delicate foxglove or the humble cow parsley, wildflowers help support the 1,500 species of pollinator in the UK, offering food and shelter for insect pollinators such as bees and butterflies. And the more diverse a meadow's wildflower species is, the larger the diversity of pollinators that visit them, also helping to maintain insectivore populations.

Ecologically productive as they may be, these types of meadows typically grow in unproductive soil. Soils that are shallow, poor at holding water or acidic are categorised as unproductive. Grass species in particular can dominate a meadow with productive soils, out competing wildflowers such as bluebells. Yet despite this, wildflowers have adapted to thrive in these harsher conditions to keep the competition at bay.

However, these flower-rich fields have been declining dramatically. Around 97 per cent of UK wildflower meadows have been lost since the 1930s, occupying only one per cent of the UK's land area. This is a result of agricultural progress and land development. The introductions of livestock farming and herbicides have contributed to the removal of wildflower meadows, while the use of fertilisers has allowed surrounding soil to become more productive, meaning dominant grass species can threaten wildflowers. The development of roads and residential homes has also played a part in this concerning decline.

Ecological charities and organisations such as Plantlife and Kew Gardens campaign to reclaim wildflower meadows in the UK. From protecting wildflower roadside verges to making our gardens more 'wild', these efforts aim to support the declining pollinator populations.

Insects contribute to the majority of the pollination of wildflower meadows

Wildflowers act as a habitat for a range of species, including the harvest mouse

"97 per cent of UK wildflower meadows have been lost since the 1930s"

Make your own meadow

Here are seven steps to help you grow your own wildflower meadow:

1 The right space
Use a section of lawn or an old flowerbed, the bigger the better.

2 Digging up
Reduce the quality of your soil by removing the topsoil (around 15 centimetres) to rid the soil of any fertilisers.

3 Turning over
Dig and turn the remaining soil until it is fine.

4 An autumnal affair
The best time to sow wildflower seeds is during the autumn season.

5 Spotting your seeds
Use a pale coloured sand to top off the turned soil, but don't use builder's sand. This will allow you to see where you have sown your wildflower mix.

6 Use your feet
Don't rake or cover the seeds with soil — simply tread them into the ground so they come into contact with the soil.

7 A midsummer trim
Once your wildflower meadow has started to bloom don't mow it until midsummer.

Meet the world's largest rodent

With dog-sized bodies, guinea-pig-like faces and feet like a duck's, capybaras are undeniably unique

It's not hard to see why capybaras were originally thought to be a sort of fuzzy pig – standing up to 60 centimetres tall and with a block-like head and no tail, they're not immediately recognisable as rodents. These strange-looking animals live in South America, always near water. Capybaras need rivers and lakes to keep their dry skin healthy and to provide them with food in the form of water plants. Webbed feet help them to move through the water and – just like hippos – their ears, eyes and nostrils are all at the top of their head, so they can submerge almost all of their body if a predator approaches.

Capybaras are known for their gentle and sociable natures. A typical group has about ten members, but they've been observed hanging out in groups of up to 100 in the dry season. They're most active at dawn and dusk but will wait until darkness falls to sneak into the water for a meal if they don't feel safe. Like other rodents, capybaras have teeth that grow constantly to cope with all the chewing – because they're so big, they can chomp their way through 3.6 kilograms of vegetation in a day.

Capybaras are placid creatures, happy to let birds rest on them and eat insects from their fur

Young capybaras learn quickly from their mothers, following them on land and in the water

What makes a wave break?

Find out what happens when the ocean meets the shore

Waves are formed when the wind blows over the surface of the sea. Energy from the wind sets particles in the water rotating around each other, creating a wave that can roll for several kilometres. When the wave reaches the shore and the water becomes shallower, friction from the seabed begins to slow it down. It loses energy from the bottom first, causing it to bunch up on itself and get taller until the back of the wave overtakes the rest and breaks into whitewash. On gently sloping shores the wave simply spills over, but steep slopes create dramatic crashing waves.

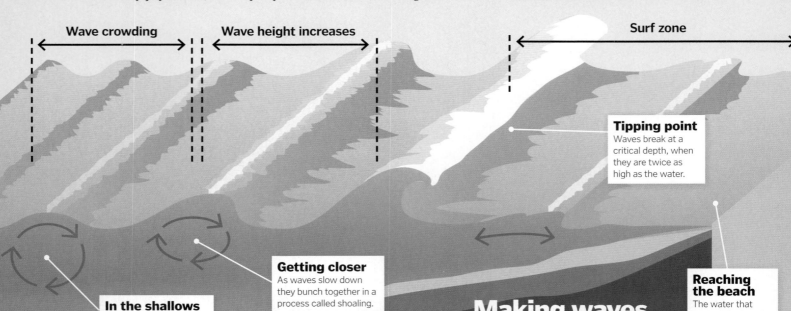

Wave crowding

Wave height increases

Surf zone

Tipping point
Waves break at a critical depth, when they are twice as high as the water.

Getting closer
As waves slow down they bunch together in a process called shoaling.

In the shallows
When they approach the shore, waves begin to lose energy.

Making waves
Take a peek under the water to see what brings waves crashing down

Reaching the beach
The water that runs up the beach after a wave breaks is called the swash.

The world's largest waterfall

Discover why you might struggle to visit the tallest waterfall on Earth

With their staggering power and awe-inspiring beauty, waterfalls are one of the most popular natural wonders to visit on Earth. However, if you were hoping to see the world's tallest waterfall, then you'd better pack your diving gear.

While most people think of Venezuela's Angel Falls as the largest waterfall in the world, that title actually goes to a ridge beneath the Denmark Strait. Here, starting 600 metres below the water's surface, is a waterfall that plunges 3,505 metres to the seafloor.

This underwater cascade is made possible due to differing water densities. In the strip of sea between Greenland and Iceland, cold waters from the north meet warmer waters from the south. The molecules in cold water are less active and more tightly packed together than those in warm water, making them much denser. Therefore, when the two meet, the cold water sinks below the warm water, where it flows over an enormous ridge to create an undersea waterfall.

As well as being incredibly tall, the Denmark Strait waterfall is also very wide, stretching 160 kilometres across. It really would be an incredible sight to behold on land, but unfortunately, as it is already surrounded by water, the falls are completely undetectable without scientific equipment. So maybe hold off on packing your bags just yet!

Under the sea
How an enormous waterfall flows beneath the waves

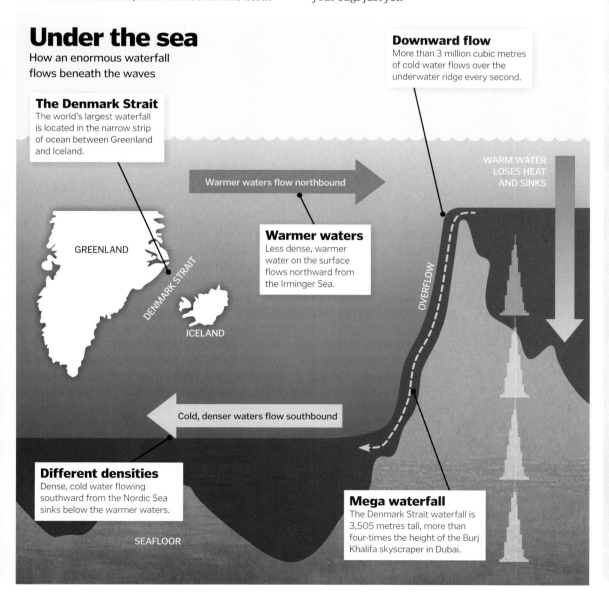

Downward flow
More than 3 million cubic metres of cold water flows over the underwater ridge every second.

The Denmark Strait
The world's largest waterfall is located in the narrow strip of ocean between Greenland and Iceland.

Warmer waters flow northbound

WARM WATER LOSES HEAT AND SINKS

Warmer waters
Less dense, warmer water on the surface flows northward from the Irminger Sea.

GREENLAND

DENMARK STRAIT

ICELAND

OVERFLOW

Cold, denser waters flow southbound

Different densities
Dense, cold water flowing southward from the Nordic Sea sinks below the warmer waters.

Mega waterfall
The Denmark Strait waterfall is 3,505 metres tall, more than four-times the height of the Burj Khalifa skyscraper in Dubai.

SEAFLOOR

5 WHOPPING WATERFALLS

1 Angel Falls – Venezuela
The tallest waterfall on land is 979m tall, three-times shorter than the Denmark Strait falls.

2 Inga Falls – DR Congo
25,768m³ of water flows over the world's largest waterfall by volume every second – equating to over 2.2bn m³ a day!

3 Khone Falls – Laos
The widest land waterfall in the world measures an incredible 10,783m across.

4 Niagara Falls – Canada-US
The world's most-visited waterfall attracts around 28 million people each year.

5 Boyoma Falls – DR Congo
The fastest waterfall has a mean annual flow rate of 17,000m³ of water per second.

SUPER VOLCANOES

Words by **Laura Mears**

The world's largest and deadliest volcanoes could envelop the whole planet in ash

Supervolcanoes are some of the most destructive natural structures on the planet. Classified only after they have erupted, they eject more than 1,000 cubic kilometres of lava in one go. They're a thousand times more powerful than a standard volcano and so large that they could blanket the whole Earth in ash.

The ground collapses above them when they explode, and the scars that mark their positions consume so much of the landscape that they become virtually invisible. Yet bubbling pools of magma still seethe below the surface, venting hot steam and gas through the ever-weakening crust above.

Scientists grade volcanic eruptions on a scale of 0 to 8, known as the Volcanic Explosivity Index (VEI). The tiniest volcanoes at the bottom of the scale gently dribble magma, while the behemoths at the top spit out hundreds of tons at a time. There are only around 40 of these supervolcanoes worldwide, but just ten remain potentially active. They sit atop hotspots where magma leaks up from the Earth's mantle. Bubbles of molten rock accumulate under the ground, building pressure that stretches the Earth at its seams. Between major eruptions, pockets of heat leak out as spurts of lava, water and gas, but eventually the pressure

becomes too much. The crust melts and cracks, heaving above the liquid rock below.

When supervolcanoes erupt in earnest the impact is catastrophic. Lava explodes upwards or bursts out in sheets, forming vast splatters and fast-moving lava plains. The temperature of the liquid rock can be as low as 300 degrees Celsius or as high as 1,160 degrees Celsius. It might advance slower than walking speed or vent at more than 60 kilometres per hour, and it tears through everything in its path.

Alongside the lava, supervolcanoes spew gas and ash. The heaviest particles settle within days, forming a blanket around the eruption that can be tens of centimetres thick. They smother crops and damage the eyes and lungs of animals.

Up in the sky, sulphur compounds react with the air, creating clouds that then unleash acid rain. Pollution races through the watercourse, impacting wildlife far from the source of the eruption. Tiny fragments of ash can remain airborne for months, scattering the sunlight and changing the climate across the globe.

Luckily, supervolcano eruptions are rare; hundreds of

As of May 2018, over 1,700 residents on Hawaii's Big Island have been evacuated following the eruption of Mount Kilauea

Kilauea is one of the most active volcanoes on Earth, but most of its eruptions are only VEI 0-1

Birth of a supervolcano
How a caldera forms, step-by-step

1 Hotspot
Intense heat in the Earth's mantle forces magma upwards.

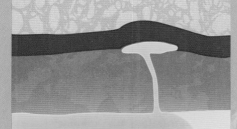

2 Bulge
As magma gathers under the crust, a chamber starts to form.

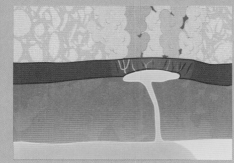

3 Cracking
Stress weakens the ground above the chamber, forming cracks.

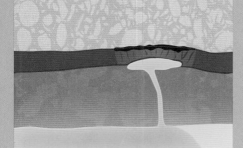

4 Collapse
The ground collapses, revealing the molten rock below.

thousands of years can go by between major events. As a result, predicting the next one is a major challenge. For this scientists use an arsenal of tools. The most basic are cameras, which are used to watch volcanoes in real time. Some are on the ground, others on satellites. They capture stills and video and scan the volcanoes in infrared to track their hotspots. Then there are seismometers, which detect motion in the ground. These usually measure in three directions: up and down, north and south, east and west.

There are more than 100 seismic recording stations worldwide, each one feeding data into a vast international network. Together they keep tabs on quakes and tremors that rip through the Earth when rocks and magma move. Seismometers not only reveal the origin, depth and magnitude of earthquakes; they also work as a 3D volcano scanner. Vibrations travel through different materials at different speeds, a bit like X-rays through the human body. Seismic waves move more slowly through hot, molten rock than cold, hard rock. Watching how tremors shift across the Earth can reveal the outline of underground magma chambers.

Very low frequency (VLF) induction can supplement this data. It's the same technology used in metal detectors, and it produces maps of the ground using electromagnetism. A transmitter coil sends a

pulsing magnetic field into the ground, which interacts with anything conductive under the surface. The conductive material makes weak magnetic fields in return, sending signals back to a receiver coil. The changing signal across the ground reveals the shape of magma lakes and flows below.

When an eruption is imminent, the volcano will start to bulge. Scientists can track this using GPS and electronic distance measuring (EDM). GPS satellites ping radio waves from all angles to create millimetre-accurate maps of volcano outlines, while EDM uses infrared light to map the flanks of the volcano from the ground. Tilt-meters, or electronic spirit levels, can add real-time feedback around the volcano rim.

Active volcanoes also start to vent more gas as they approach an eruption, and this is detectable with a correlation spectrometer (COSPEC). These devices look at the light coming through plumes of volcanic gas and compare it to the light moving through normal air. This reveals how much gas is coming out of a volcano.

To really understand the potential of active supervolcanoes we also need to trace their history. Fortunately, the impact of past eruptions is still visible in ancient rock. When supervolcanoes explode they spit hundreds of cubic kilometres of material into the air, and this leaves its trace on the

ground. Geologists look for vast calderas and spurts of lava hardened into spokes or plains. Their position reveals their age, and analysis of their chemical composition tells us much about their history.

Supervolcanoes are so colossal that signs of their eruptions appear across the world. Ice at the poles has trapped particles from ancient eruptions, and cores drilled from the Arctic and Antarctic are a valuable source of volcano history. Scientists crush the ice inch by inch in sterile lab conditions, collecting trapped sediments and bubbles of air. These then pass through spectrometers, chromatographs and microscopes to identify the particles and reveal the culprit.

Data like this from past eruptions can help scientists to map 'at-risk' areas. Though we can't yet prevent supervolcano eruptions, understanding the lava, ash, gas, mud and flooding that they can produce will help us to prepare for the future.

"Tiny fragments of ash can remain airborne for months"

© Getty; SPL; Alamy

Know your volcanoes

Different types of volcano erupt in dramatically different ways

Plinian
Violent jets shoot into the atmosphere, triggering vast lightning storms.

Icelandic
Fissures open up in the ground, leaking horizontally to form flat lava plains.

Dome
Slow-moving lava piles up at the mouth of the volcano.

Pelean
Flows ooze down the sides of the volcano, destroying everything in their path.

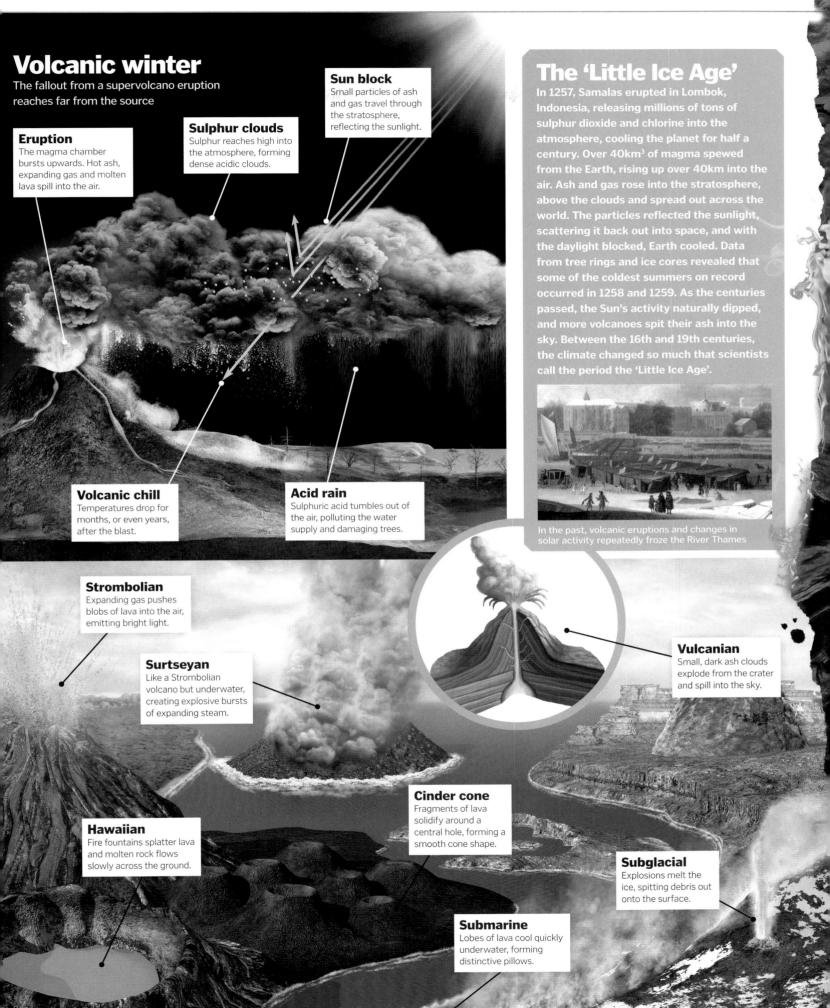

Volcanic winter
The fallout from a supervolcano eruption reaches far from the source

Eruption
The magma chamber bursts upwards. Hot ash, expanding gas and molten lava spill into the air.

Sulphur clouds
Sulphur reaches high into the atmosphere, forming dense acidic clouds.

Sun block
Small particles of ash and gas travel through the stratosphere, reflecting the sunlight.

Volcanic chill
Temperatures drop for months, or even years, after the blast.

Acid rain
Sulphuric acid tumbles out of the air, polluting the water supply and damaging trees.

The 'Little Ice Age'
In 1257, Samalas erupted in Lombok, Indonesia, releasing millions of tons of sulphur dioxide and chlorine into the atmosphere, cooling the planet for half a century. Over 40km³ of magma spewed from the Earth, rising up over 40km into the air. Ash and gas rose into the stratosphere, above the clouds and spread out across the world. The particles reflected the sunlight, scattering it back out into space, and with the daylight blocked, Earth cooled. Data from tree rings and ice cores revealed that some of the coldest summers on record occurred in 1258 and 1259. As the centuries passed, the Sun's activity naturally dipped, and more volcanoes spit their ash into the sky. Between the 16th and 19th centuries, the climate changed so much that scientists call the period the 'Little Ice Age'.

In the past, volcanic eruptions and changes in solar activity repeatedly froze the River Thames

Strombolian
Expanding gas pushes blobs of lava into the air, emitting bright light.

Surtseyan
Like a Strombolian volcano but underwater, creating explosive bursts of expanding steam.

Hawaiian
Fire fountains splatter lava and molten rock flows slowly across the ground.

Cinder cone
Fragments of lava solidify around a central hole, forming a smooth cone shape.

Vulcanian
Small, dark ash clouds explode from the crater and spill into the sky.

Subglacial
Explosions melt the ice, spitting debris out onto the surface.

Submarine
Lobes of lava cool quickly underwater, forming distinctive pillows.

What lies beneath

Under Yellowstone's picturesque park, monstrous magma chambers lurk...

Hot water bubbles up as violent geysers in Yellowstone National Park

Tectonic activity

The North American tectonic plate moves around 2.5cm to the southwest each year, while the base of the plume stays put.

Plate

Mantle plume

16 million years ago

Rising heat from the mantle plume melted the crust above it, generating the hotspot's first eruption.

12–7 million years ago

Further eruptions created more calderas, which drifted as the plate moved southwest. Ancient calderas from this hotspot can now be found in Nevada and Oregon.

2.1 million years ago

The Huckleberry Ridge eruption spewed out an estimated 2,500km³ of rock, lava and ash – the largest known eruption in the hotspot's history.

Yellowstone calderas

Several overlapping calderas mark the sites of Yellowstone's previous eruptions; the most recent formed around 640,000 years ago.

Picabo caldera
10.3 million years ago

Big Bend Ridge caldera
2.1 million years ago

Yellowstone caldera
640,000 years ago

YELLOWSTONE NATIONAL PARK

Geothermal activity

Heat from the magma reservoirs powers the park's 10,000+ hydrothermal features, including geysers and hot springs.

Magma reservoirs

Two large pockets of magma lie below Yellowstone. They obtain their heat from the massive mantle plume below.

Upper crustal magma reservoir
760°C

Lower crustal magma reservoir
980°C

Mantle plume
1200°C

"Currently, there is nothing we can do to stop a supervolcano"

Is Yellowstone about to blow?

The world's most infamous volcano sleeps fitfully under a national park in Wyoming and Montana. Yellowstone has burst through the Earth three times in the past 2.1 million years, leaving vast scars on the landscape. The most recent eruption (640,000 years ago) left a 2,400-square-kilometre hole in the ground. Since then there have been at least 80 smaller eruptions, and the volcano remains active to this day.

Each year more than 1,000 earthquakes shake the park, and the surrounding ground still boils and hisses, venting gas and water into the air. Analysis of the area suggests that large eruptions happen every 600,000–800,000 years. With the last major outburst sitting squarely within that bracket, there has been much speculation about when the next one will occur. According to the US Geological Survey, a Yellowstone eruption would blanket everything within a 320-kilometre radius knee-deep in ash.

Monitoring stations are listening for signs of an impending explosion. Daily tremors should increase, becoming stronger and closer together. The ground will start to shift, creaking, cracking and bulging under the stress. Currently, there is nothing we can do to stop a supervolcano eruption, but NASA has an intriguing idea. Yellowstone vents increase their heat and pressure level by spitting water up to the surface, so drilling down into the volcano and pumping more water into the rock might help to cool it down. As a bonus, the steam could drive a geothermal power plant.

It's still just an idea, but at the moment there's no great rush. According to the National Park Service, an eruption in the next 1,000–10,000 years is very unlikely.

Yellowstone's hot springs are fuelled by the magma chambers below

Trail of evidence
As the tectonic plate drifted, new areas of the crust were positioned over the hotspot. Evidence of past eruptions can be tracked along the Snake River Plain, which stretches from Wyoming through Idaho to Oregon and Nevada.

Bruneau-Jarbidge caldera 12.5 million years ago
Twin Falls caldera 10–8.6 million years ago
Heise caldera 6–4.3 million years ago

Mega-plume
The magma plume below Yellowstone may extend as far as 2,900km deep, down to the boundary between Earth's mantle and the outer core.

Mantle monster
The region's hotspot is the result of a huge mantle plume. Both the plume and the reservoirs above it consist of superheated molten rock.

CRUST
YELLOWSTONE NATIONAL PARK
UPPER MANTLE
40km
1,600km
SCALE (km)
0
1,600 MANTLE
2,900 OUTER CORE
5,150
6,400 INNER CORE

© Nat Geo, Getty

The world's deadliest volcanoes

These 14 mountains are responsible for some of the largest eruptions in history

"There are more than 100 seismic recording stations worldwide"

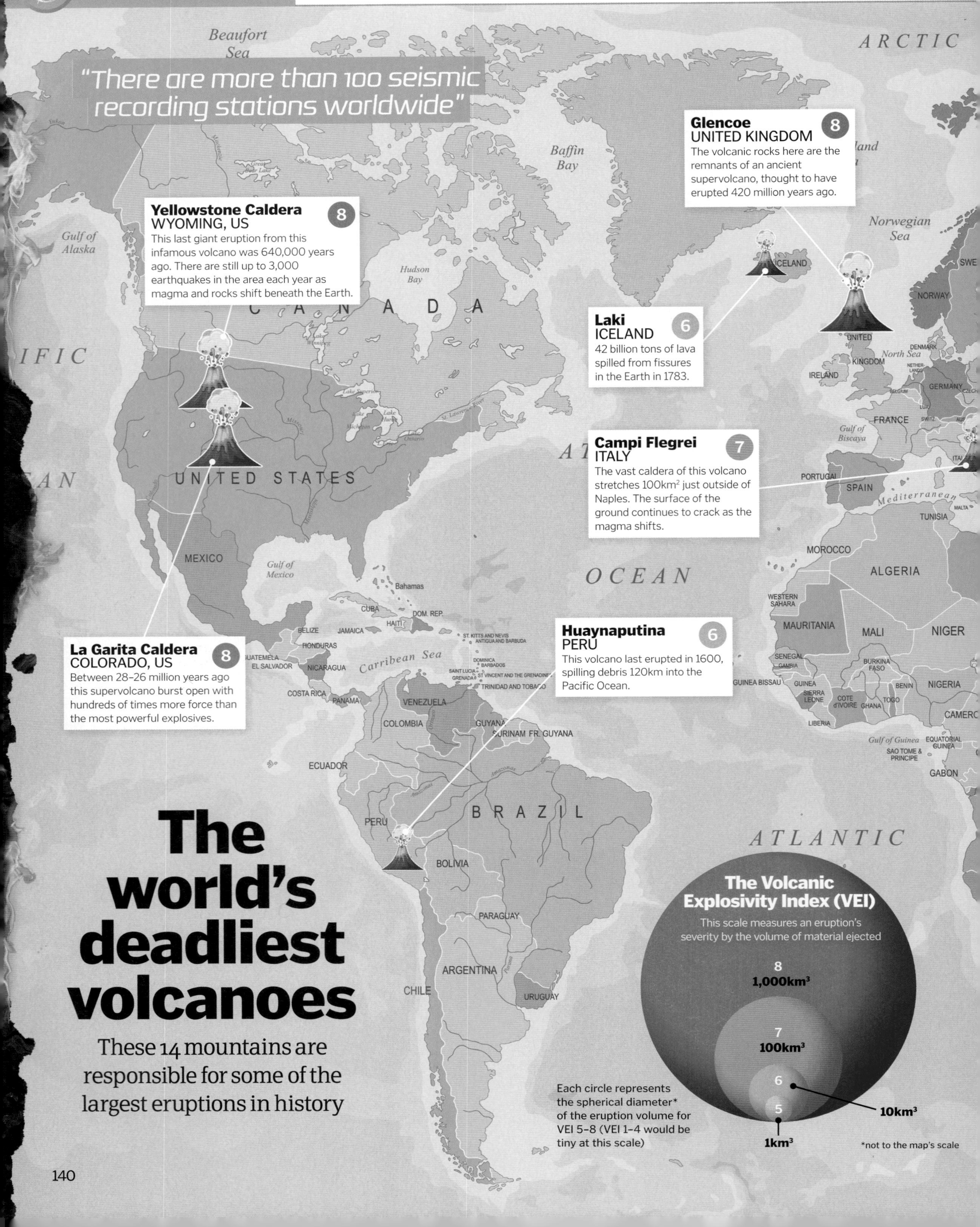

Yellowstone Caldera 8
WYOMING, US
This last giant eruption from this infamous volcano was 640,000 years ago. There are still up to 3,000 earthquakes in the area each year as magma and rocks shift beneath the Earth.

La Garita Caldera 8
COLORADO, US
Between 28–26 million years ago this supervolcano burst open with hundreds of times more force than the most powerful explosives.

Glencoe 8
UNITED KINGDOM
The volcanic rocks here are the remnants of an ancient supervolcano, thought to have erupted 420 million years ago.

Laki 6
ICELAND
42 billion tons of lava spilled from fissures in the Earth in 1783.

Campi Flegrei 7
ITALY
The vast caldera of this volcano stretches 100km² just outside of Naples. The surface of the ground continues to crack as the magma shifts.

Huaynaputina 6
PERU
This volcano last erupted in 1600, spilling debris 120km into the Pacific Ocean.

The Volcanic Explosivity Index (VEI)

This scale measures an eruption's severity by the volume of material ejected

8 — 1,000km³
7 — 100km³
6 — 10km³
5 — 1km³

Each circle represents the spherical diameter* of the eruption volume for VEI 5–8 (VEI 1–4 would be tiny at this scale)

*not to the map's scale

Vesuvius
ITALY (5)
This infamous volcano buried the town of Pompeii when it erupted in 79 CE.

Etna
ITALY (5)
The most active volcano in Europe often spits lava into the air.

Thera
GREECE (7)
This island volcano may have buried a city (perhaps inspiring the myth of Atlantis) when it erupted in 1620 BCE.

Pinatubo
PHILIPPINES (6)
Scientists predicted the 1991 eruption of this volcano, saving over 5,000 lives.

Toba
INDONESIA (8)
Four monumental eruptions formed Lake Toba. The island at its centre is a mountain of solid magma, pushed up through the caldera by the pressure beneath.

Tambora
INDONESIA (7)
In 1815, this super-colossal volcano entered the record books with the largest eruption ever recorded. It spewed so much ash into the air that there was no summer the following year.

Krakatoa
INDONESIA (6)
This colossal volcano erupted in 1883, creating waves that killed more than 36,000 people.

Taupo
NEW ZEALAND (8)
The most recent supervolcano eruption came from this lakebed in New Zealand 1,800 years ago. The magma chamber sits around 7km under the water.

The heart of a supervolcano contains a bubbling magma chamber

© Getty

HISTORY

144
The Silk Road

148
Prehistoric wildlife

150
Brunel's block machines

"Even at low tide the exposed sand flats were treacherous to cross"

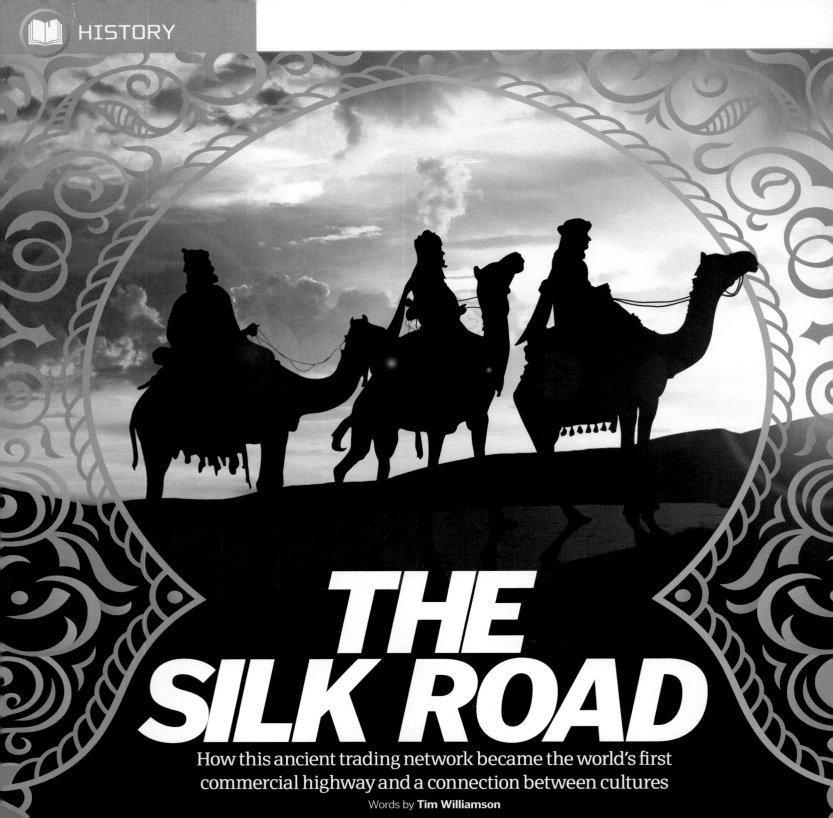

THE SILK ROAD

How this ancient trading network became the world's first commercial highway and a connection between cultures

Words by **Tim Williamson**

For the average medieval European peasant, the far-off lands of Persia and China were only heard of in stories, and few could even dream of travelling there. Despite this, they might have been more familiar with the sight of the few exotic goods arriving in Europe from Eastern trade routes.

By the late Middle Ages, items such as jade, spices, tea, precious metals and silk could be found for sale in bustling European market cities. Many different trade routes had developed between China and the West over the centuries, beginning as early as around

125 BCE when the Chinese Han dynasty began searching far beyond its borders for new trading opportunities. In the 19th century these routes, which stretched over thousands of kilometres and connected two continents, were nicknamed the Silk Roads after the unique export that the Western world craved.

Silk was first produced in China as far back as 2700 BCE, and for a long time it was the exclusive luxury of the Chinese royal family. For this reason, the method of its production remained a closely guarded secret for centuries. However, by the 2nd century BCE

the export of silk gradually became permitted. Emperor Wudi allowed silk to be traded for valuable war horses – something the Chinese military desperately needed to help defend their borders. The Yuezhi tribes with whom they traded lived in the western regions of the empire in the Fergana Valley. These exchanges formed the first building blocks of the Silk Road.

It was around this period that the Roman Republic, and later the Empire, was growing in strength and expanding its territory eastwards from the Mediterranean Sea

During military campaigns against the Parthian Empire (which today is the region of Iran, Iraq and Syria) in the 1st century BCE, the Romans observed the silk banners of their enemy and were fascinated by this unfamiliar material that was both strong yet delicate to the touch. The Roman aristocracy soon became obsessed with silk garments and created a great demand for this must-have fabric. Inevitably, these luxury products brought in a premium profit for merchants, but transporting the goods across thousands of miles of challenging terrain was no mean feat.

After leaving the Chinese capital of Chang'an – the heart of silk production in this period – travelling convoys or caravans were forced to traverse around deserts and mountains with their wares. The rough terrain beyond the safety of city walls was perfect for marauding bandits, who stalked the routes the caravans were known to take. Sections of China's Great Wall were extended to protect weak points along the roads, and armed garrisons were stationed in key towns.

Upon arriving safely at the next trading post, town or city, merchants would often sell or barter their wares rather than continuing on the journey west. On the far western Chinese border, Kashgar was one such profitable stop, where traders travelling from the Indian peninsula, Persia and beyond would gather to buy and sell. In this way the merchants themselves didn't have to risk the long and perilous journeys, but their goods continued onwards along a chain of different owners.

Eventually, the road reached the Parthian Empire, a vast state that was neighbour to both

Roman territory and the regions to the east, occupying a midway point along the Silk Roads. Realising the high demand for Chinese goods in the West, the Parthians were able to raise the price on silk sold in their lands, especially to European merchants travelling from Rome and elsewhere. The Parthian capital of Ctesiphon served as a major trading hub, where goods could be exchanged before travelling across the deserts of Mesopotamia strapped to the backs of camels. Palmyra and Damascus were key stop-off points on the way to the ports of Antioch or Tyre before passage across the Mediterranean and Europe.

Of course, not all routes between the East and West were land roads. Sea routes traversing the Indian peninsula in particular were popular with spice traders. Cinnamon, pepper, ginger, nutmeg, saffron and other goods crossed some 15,000 kilometres of sea routes between the Arabian peninsula and as far as Japan and the islands of the Philippines.

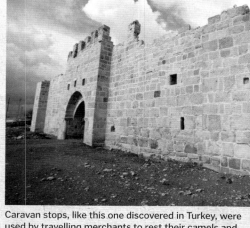

Caravan stops, like this one discovered in Turkey, were used by travelling merchants to rest their camels and trade their wares

For centuries, silk was exclusively produced in China and was highly sought after in the West

A depiction of Marco Polo travelling within a trading caravan

Marco Polo

Born into a prosperous Venetian family in 1254, Marco Polo was one of the most famous explorers of the late Middle Ages. His father and uncle, Niccolò and Maffeo, both successful jewel merchants, joined a diplomatic mission to the court of the Mongol emperor Kublai Khan in 1260, arriving back in Venice in 1269. On their next journey two years later they took young Marco with them. Between 1271 and 1295 the group travelled across Persia and Asia to Khanbalik (now Beijing) and Khan's court.

Shortly after returning to Venice from his 24-year round trip, Marco was captured by Venice's rival city state, Genoa. However, it was while in captivity that his adventures were first written down. The finished book, *The Travels of Marco Polo*, gives the earliest detailed accounts of European interactions with and impressions of Asian societies and cultures.

Many of these products found their way into the Mediterranean through southern routes via the Red Sea, eventually entering into the bustling markets of Italian trading hubs such as Venice and Genoa. As navigation techniques improved and new hull designs produced faster ships, this route by sea became more and more popular, despite the occasional threat from pirates. As the centuries passed these 'sea roads' became even more preferable, as warring countries occasionally shut down or embargoed the flow of trade.

Back on land, travellers along the road were increasingly carrying with them ideas, philosophies and religious beliefs unheard of in the regions through which they travelled, often with the intention of converting others to their faith. Buddhism first arrived in China across the southern routes leading to India, and likewise Islam and Christianity arrived from the western routes. Soon pilgrims, missionaries, preachers and explorers were common sights on the caravan paths.

It was around the 13th century that the secret of silk production was finally smuggled back to Europe by Christian missionaries. Two Franciscan friars learned the centuries-old Chinese methods and the secret of the silkworm. It was also around this period that the famous explorer Marco Polo was trekking to and from the Mongol court in the far east of China, bringing back with him detailed accounts and stories of his experiences. Rather than the generation of huge profits, it is this mass cultural exchange over centuries that makes the Silk Roads so significant in world history.

The route to the East
Traders used several different paths to transport their precious cargo

Gateway to the West
Major Italian port cities such as Venice or Genoa were often the final destination for merchants travelling with goods from the eastern routes.

Silk routes
Eurasian Steppe Route
Other trade routes
Spice routes (maritime)
Great Wall of China
Incense road

The sea road
Merchants dealing in spices found passage to the East via the Nile and the Red Sea, avoiding the deserts and mountains to the northeast.

Middle East empires
The cities of Ctesiphon, Damascus and Tyre were all major trading points within the borders of the Parthian, Seleucid and later the Sasanian empires.

A deadly export
The horrific bubonic plague, also known as the Black Death, killed millions of Europeans during the 14th century and is thought to have spread via trade ships and busy port towns. However, recent research has suggested that strains of the disease might have travelled even further.

Scientists studying victims of a deadly plague in 19th-century China and the European victims of the 14th-century Black Death have found a startling similarity in the DNA pattern of the two diseases. This suggests the plague not only could have travelled across the Silk Roads heading east but may have been dormant for centuries before being unleashed in another outbreak, long after the original Black Death.

Tens of millions of people died as a result of the Black Death in medieval Europe

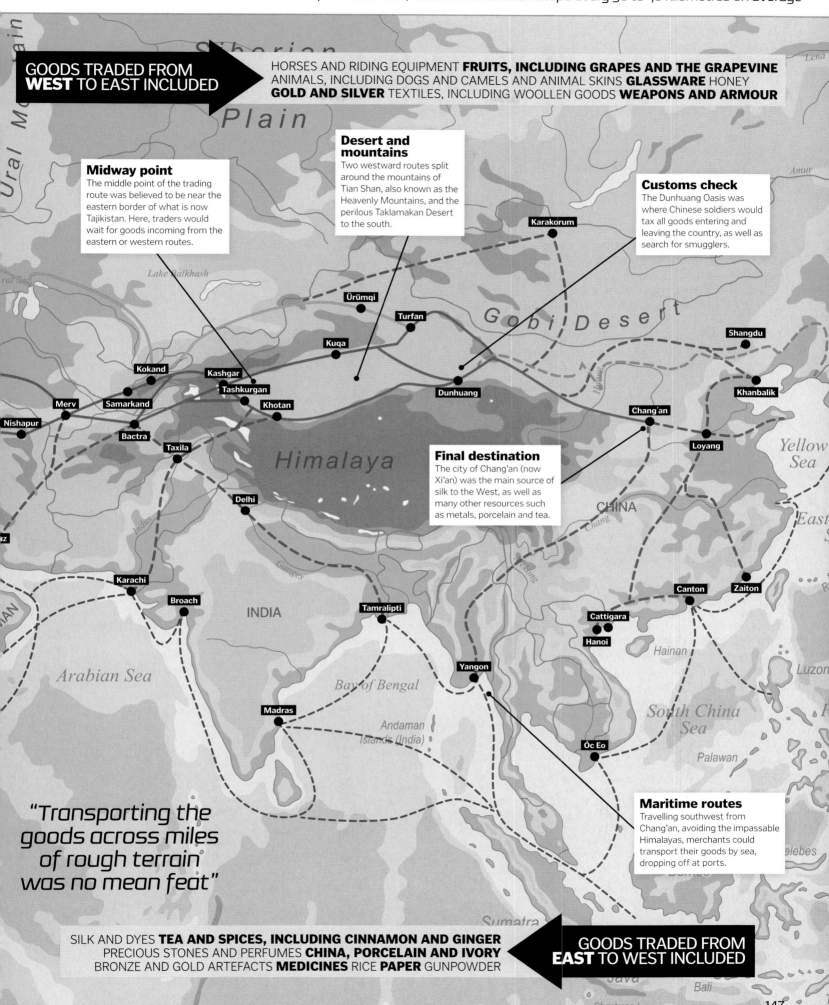

GOODS TRADED FROM WEST TO EAST INCLUDED

HORSES AND RIDING EQUIPMENT **FRUITS, INCLUDING GRAPES AND THE GRAPEVINE** ANIMALS, INCLUDING DOGS AND CAMELS AND ANIMAL SKINS **GLASSWARE** HONEY **GOLD AND SILVER** TEXTILES, INCLUDING WOOLLEN GOODS **WEAPONS AND ARMOUR**

Midway point
The middle point of the trading route was believed to be near the eastern border of what is now Tajikistan. Here, traders would wait for goods incoming from the eastern or western routes.

Desert and mountains
Two westward routes split around the mountains of Tian Shan, also known as the Heavenly Mountains, and the perilous Taklamakan Desert to the south.

Customs check
The Dunhuang Oasis was where Chinese soldiers would tax all goods entering and leaving the country, as well as search for smugglers.

Final destination
The city of Chang'an (now Xi'an) was the main source of silk to the West, as well as many other resources such as metals, porcelain and tea.

Maritime routes
Travelling southwest from Chang'an, avoiding the impassable Himalayas, merchants could transport their goods by sea, dropping off at ports.

"Transporting the goods across miles of rough terrain was no mean feat"

SILK AND DYES **TEA AND SPICES, INCLUDING CINNAMON AND GINGER** PRECIOUS STONES AND PERFUMES **CHINA, PORCELAIN AND IVORY** BRONZE AND GOLD ARTEFACTS **MEDICINES** RICE **PAPER** GUNPOWDER

GOODS TRADED FROM EAST TO WEST INCLUDED

Prehistoric wildlife

This fossil proved that life existed around 560 million years ago

Fossils of charnia have been found all around the world

5 45 million years ago there was no life on land, but the oceans were teeming with it. So many fossil finds date to this point in history – the Cambrian period – that scientists believed no organisms existed earlier. This theory was disproved in 1957 after a schoolboy made a startling discovery.

Roger Mason came across a leaf-like fossil in Charnwood Forest, UK, a species that became known as *Charnia masoni*. The fossil was found within rocks that were pre-Cambrian, proving that life was far more ancient than previously thought. Decades earlier, Charles Darwin had predicted that life existed before the Cambrian age – finally here was the proof.

Charnia is believed to have been rooted to the ocean floor, feeding on microbes in the water. It had a quilted body that some experts believe may have stored algae, giving it a green colour that enabled it to gather energy from sunlight through photosynthesis.

Fossils from other pre-Cambrian creatures are rare as their squishy bodies could only fossilise under precise conditions. Some of these ocean dwellers evolved shells and skeletons during the Cambrian era, which explains the abundance of fossils and the long-held idea of an explosion of life at this time.

Charnia lived on the seafloor, perhaps feeding on microbes

The Doomsday Clock

Why is it two minutes to midnight and what does that mean?

The Doomsday Clock was created by the *Bulletin of the Atomic Scientists* (BAS) in 1947 to symbolise the urgency of a nuclear threat. The hands of a clock ticking down to midnight were shown on the magazine's cover, like the countdown of an atomic bomb. It was the idea of a group of scientists who had participated in the Manhattan Project – an American-led scheme to develop the first nuclear weapons during World War Two.

Since then, the Doomsday Clock has continually been updated, but it now alerts the public to other dangers such as climate change and cyber warfare. It is now just two minutes to midnight and nuclear threats have taken centre stage once again.

Physicist Dr Leon Lederman adjusts the hands of the Doomsday Clock in 2002

1947	1953	1963	1974	1984	1991	2018
The Doomsday Clock appears for the first time, triggered by Cold War tensions and the threat of nuclear dangers.	The United States and Soviet Union test hydrogen bombs, weapons more powerful than any atomic bombs.	The Partial Test Ban Treaty is signed and ends all atmospheric nuclear testing, slowing the arms race.	The US and Soviet Union appear to be modernising their nuclear forces, while other nations increase their nuclear capabilities.	There are worries that a new arms race will begin after relations between the US and the Soviet Union break down.	With the Cold War officially over, the Strategic Arms Reduction Treaty reduces the number of US and Russian nuclear weapons.	The threat of nuclear war, rising tensions between nations and climate change push the clock closer to midnight.

1953
2018
1984
1947
1974
1963
1991

12
9

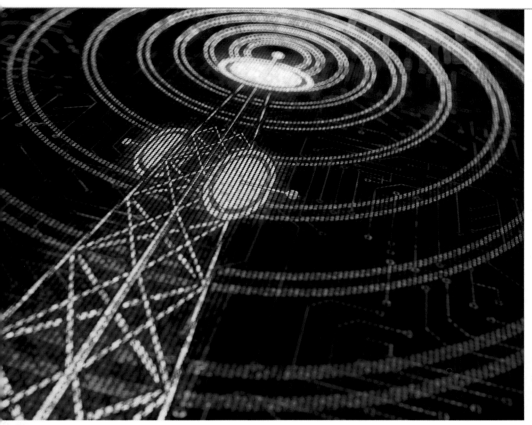

Russia's ghost radio station

A mysterious shortwave signal is broadcasting
an eerie buzz, but nobody knows why

A short, monotonous buzz being broadcast 24 hours a day is currently being emitted from a radio station at an unknown location in Russia. The mysterious sound repeats at a rate of 25 times a minute, broken only by the occasional live Russian voice transmission. Is the signal used for military communications, perhaps just a channel marker to keep the frequency busy so it is easier to use? Or is the sound the result of something more sinister? The earliest known recording has been dated to 1982, and many theories have been proposed since then.

Its original call sign was UVB-76, but today the tower uses ZhUOZ. The buzz is broken by Russian words, but they offer no real clue as to the function of the radio or its origins. They are often common nouns, including 'virus' and 'prison'. It sounds like a

code, but the Russian military claim they have nothing to do with the mysterious signal.

Perhaps the most chilling theory is that the tone might be what is known as a 'Dead Hand' signal, a system designed to automatically retaliate with deadly nuclear strikes in response to a nuclear attack on Russia, which would be picked up by radio wave interference. This system was first devised by the Soviet Union during the Cold War era, and some experts suggest it may still be in use today.

Regardless of its origins, there must be someone behind the signal and there must be someone tuning into the live transmission who knows the real reason why the broadcast is being sent out. The question is who?

The exact source location of the signal is unknown, and it's thought to have moved on at least one occasion

Clues from the buzzer

The only clues about the purpose of this tower come from the sound of the signal itself. We know that the buzz continues 24 hours a day, seven days a week, 365 days a year, and it has done so for at least three decades. During this time the sound has altered occasionally and sometimes even paused for brief periods, but it has never fully stopped.

We know that UVB-76 became more vocal after the fall of communism in Russia – which may give a hint of a political identity – and after the turn of the millennium even more communications were heard over the frequency. With the increase in global interest from radio enthusiasts, it has become evident the sound isn't recorded. Instead, it is being created manually by a tonewheel and picked up by a microphone. If you listen long enough to the broadcast you can very occasionally hear muffled conversations or sounds of things moving in the background.

Other notable events include approximately 24 hours of eerie silence on 5 June 2010, and in September 2010 the station was moved and began to use a new call sign – MDZhB. On 11 November 2010, a conversation involving 'bridge operative officer on duty' was broadcast – it's suspected that this was accidental.

A similarly strange radio signal, broadcast from Cyprus between the 1970s and 2008, is believed to have been operated by the British Secret Intelligence Service

© Getty

149

Brunel's block machines

How one man steered the Royal Navy into the modern age

Everyone's heard of Isambard Kingdom Brunel, the man who built Britain, but did you know his father was also an extraordinary engineer? In the late 1700s the Royal Navy was struggling to expand its fleet fast enough to compete with overseas powers, and Marc Isambard Brunel came to their rescue. His patented block-making machines were the first all-metal production line and boosted efficiency in the process of making ship parts. They also enabled a precision and uniformity that was previously unheard of.

The machines were so efficient that just ten men, along with a 30-horsepower steam engine, could replicate the work of over 100. What's more, they didn't need to be skilled craftsmen to oversee the production process.

There were approximately 22 different types of machines used to complete the process, including sawing logs into blocks, drilling holes for axles and shaping the exterior. By 1805, over 40 machines were built in the Portsmouth dockyard, and by 1808 around 130,000 blocks of various sizes were produced each year. Some machines were still in operation over 150 years later. Brunel's invention kick-started the age of mass production and became the precursor to modern factories around the world.

A ship's pulley-block made by Brunel's machines

Interior of the Portsmouth Block Mills circa 1900; block making ceased production here in the mid-1960s

A drawing of some of the machinery that was installed at the dockyard, which was made by skilled tool-maker Henry Maudslay

Fore-edge painting

The tale of how books were transformed into works of art

Some centuries-old books contain more than just a story: hidden beneath their gilt edges are pieces of art that can only be revealed by bending the pages. These secret pictures are known as fore-edge paintings. The images reflect scenes described within the books themselves, and they were created by clamping the pages in a fanned position and painting miniature scenes on the margins with painstaking detail. The clamp was then released and the edges of the book were brushed with gilt to obscure the image.

This technique was developed in 17th-century England by Samuel Mearne, a bookbinder to the royal family. The trend swept the nation. Some artists even produced double fore-edge paintings, where two different images would be revealed depending on which direction you fanned the pages. Others would paint a panoramic scene along all three edges.

However, the practice actually began a century earlier when the Venetian artist Cesare Vecellio turned his pages into a canvas. Instead of concealing his masterpieces, the artist displayed his handiwork in full view for the reader. Not only did this enhance the beauty of the books, it was also easier to identify subjects on the shelf. Although the popularity of fore-edge painting has waned, there are still some specialists creating art on the edge today.

This prayer book bears a fore-edge painting, added to it in around 1930

History of the British Library

This centuries-old institution holds one of the most extensive collections of global knowledge

Although the modern British Library was established as recently as 1973, its origins stretch back as far as the 18th century. Its original collection was bequeathed to the nation for the sum of £20,000 by Sir Hans Sloane, a physician who had collected over 71,000 artefacts including manuscripts, books and coins during his lifetime. His collection was opened in 1753 in Montagu House, Bloomsbury as part of the British Museum Library, the present site of the British Museum.

In 1662 the statute of Legal Deposit was passed in England and Wales, requiring a copy of every printed publication to be given to the British Museum Library (and five other legal deposit libraries in the UK). In 1710 this statute was extended to include the whole of the UK.

In May 1857 the iconic Reading Room was opened, allowing members of the public access to the library's treasures. However, passes were soon introduced, admitting only approved members.

In the latter part of the 19th century the library's full catalogue had reached its 2,250th volume, each one of them handwritten. This was transferred into 437 printed parts over the course of around 25 years. By this time the full collection counted some 2 million printed titles.

In its new location on Euston Road, the modern British Library now houses items in most known languages and continues to house and collect not only all print material produced in the UK and Ireland but also a wide range of music and film recordings.

Over 400,000 people use the library's reading rooms each year

Many famous writers and politicians studied in the British Museum's Reading Room, including Karl Marx, Vladimir Lenin and Sir Arthur Conan Doyle

The current British Library was opened by HRH Queen Elizabeth II in June 1998

150,000,000+
The number of items currently held by the British Library

3,000,000
new items are added to the library's collection every year

625 KM
The distance covered by all the library's shelves and growing every year

If you saw five items each day it would take
80,000 years
to view the library's entire collection

225,000
Volumes lost during a German air raid in 1941

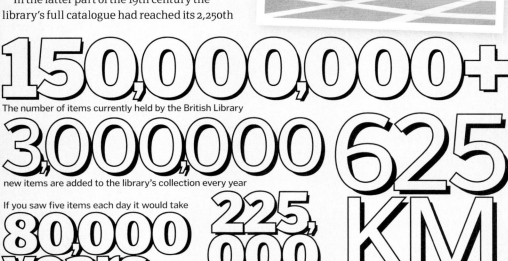

Written treasures
Discover some of the library's most valuable tomes

The world's oldest book
The British Library is home to the only known copy of the *Diamond Sutra*, a Buddhist scroll made in 868, making it the world's earliest-dated printed book.

A right royal read
The *Cotton Manuscripts* contain signed letters by Henry VIII and Elizabeth I, the personal diary of Edward VI and the last will and testament of Mary Queen of Scots.

Da Vinci's codex
Over 7,000 pages of Leonardo da Vinci's notes and drawings (including his theories and inventions) have survived and now form part of the manuscript collection within the British Library.

Captain Scott's diary
The Terra Nova Expedition (1910–13) included Captain Scott's team's attempt to reach the South Pole. They recorded their experience in his diary, which enabled their story to be told to a nation.

English heritage
Beowulf, regarded as the greatest poem in Old English, Shakespeare's *The First Folio* and two of four surviving copies of the Magna Carta 1215 are all housed at the British Library.

© Getty; Thinkstock

Hampton Court Palace

From Henry VIII's love nest to Queen Victoria's restoration project: inside the 500-year-old royal residence

One of England's most treasured historic palaces, Hampton Court was famously home to King Henry VIII, along with his many wives, lovers and scandals. However, the property was originally owned by the monarch's trusted advisor Cardinal Thomas Wolsey, before he was accused of treason and fell from favour, losing his status and stately home.

In 1529, the king and his future queen Anne Boleyn set about making a few royal redesigns. The lovers' initials were carved into the woodwork, and the new queen's lodgings were planned. However, Anne would never use these apartments, as she too fell from the king's grace. After her execution in 1536 Henry ordered that all trace of her be removed, but you can still see an interlocking 'H' and 'A' lying in a forgotten corner of the palace's Great Hall, which the pair had commissioned together.

Beyond this magnificent dining hall lay the king's private chambers, but these were later demolished by King William III and Queen Mary II between 1689–94. By this time the Tudor Gothic style was old-fashioned, so the royal couple commissioned architect Sir Christopher Wren to remodel the palace.

A sweeping staircase leads to William III's State Apartments – a series of grand rooms where he would address high-ranking courtiers. However, the king was happiest in his private apartments, including his personal study and bedroom, all lined with paintings from his collection. William and Mary also built an elaborate maze and Privy garden in Hampton Court's grounds, and they even had chocolate kitchens installed – a relatively new delicacy in England and a luxury only few could afford.

By the Georgian period Hampton Court was in decline. No British monarch lived there again after 1737, and its many apartments were awarded to courtiers – that is, until Queen Victoria ordered the gates to be 'thrown open to all her subjects' in 1838. The palace was so popular that restoration work was gradually carried out to preserve its history, and visitors still come from all over the world to follow in the footsteps of royalty.

Fountain Court

The Chapel Royal
The church has been in use ever since it was built in the 16th century. The royal family worshipped in their own private pew overlooking the main congregation.

The Great Hall
England's last medieval hall hosted magnificent royal banquets and also doubled as the staff canteen. The walls are hung with Henry's finest tapestries, *The Story of Abraham*.

Clock Court

The Kitchens
These enormous Tudor kitchens served over 1,200 meals a day! Meat was always on the menu, and 'spit boys' would roast large quantities in the huge fireplaces.

The Georgian Apartments
Built on the site of the Tudor king and queen's apartments, this was where Prince George and Princess Caroline of Wales slept, ate and entertained in extravagant Georgian style.

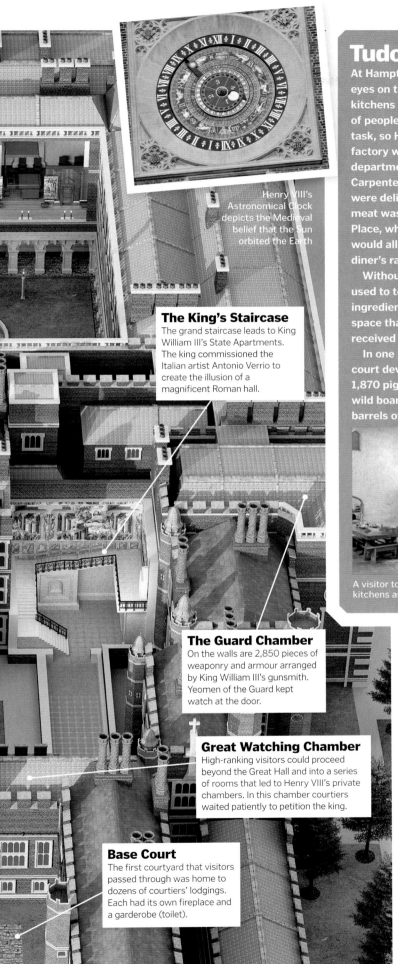

Henry VIII's Astronomical Clock depicts the Medieval belief that the Sun orbited the Earth

The King's Staircase
The grand staircase leads to King William III's State Apartments. The king commissioned the Italian artist Antonio Verrio to create the illusion of a magnificent Roman hall.

The Guard Chamber
On the walls are 2,850 pieces of weaponry and armour arranged by King William III's gunsmith. Yeomen of the Guard kept watch at the door.

Great Watching Chamber
High-ranking visitors could proceed beyond the Great Hall and into a series of rooms that led to Henry VIII's private chambers. In this chamber courtiers waited patiently to petition the king.

Base Court
The first courtyard that visitors passed through was home to dozens of courtiers' lodgings. Each had its own fireplace and a garderobe (toilet).

Tudor dining

At Hampton Court you can feast your eyes on the largest surviving Renaissance kitchens in Europe. To cater for hundreds of people twice daily was an immense task, so Henry VIII's enormous food factory was organised into various departments. These included the Master Carpenter's Court, where the supplies were delivered, the Boiling House, where meat was prepared, and the Serving Place, where the clerk of the kitchens would allocate dishes according to the diner's rank.

Without fridges, the Fish Court was used to temporarily store raw ingredients. This was a narrow, outdoor space that ran north to south, so it received little sunlight.

In one year of Elizabeth I's reign the court devoured 8,200 sheep, 2,330 deer, 1,870 pigs, 1,240 oxen, 760 calves and 53 wild boar! This was all washed down with barrels of wine, beer and ale.

A visitor to the Tudor court in 1554 described the kitchens as 'veritable hells'

"Queen Victoria ordered the gates to be 'thrown open to all her subjects'"

This maze was commissioned around 1700 by William III. It's the UK's oldest surviving hedge maze

153

The right to vote

Women have been fighting for equal rights for over a century.
Here are some of the landmark moments on the road to suffrage

New Zealand
The first country where all women could vote
New Zealand became the first self-governing country to grant the vote to all women. Years of campaigning resulted in a petition signed by over 30,000 women and the passing of the Electoral Act 1893. However, women would not gain the right to stand for parliament until 1919.

United Kingdom
British suffrage begins
British suffragettes were fiercely campaigning for women's rights under the motto 'Deeds not Words' prior to WWI. The Representation of the People Bill was passed in 1918, giving women over the age of 30 who held property the right to vote. Their rights were far from equal though, as men could vote from the age of 21, but it marked the start of women's suffrage in the UK.

Spain
Playing catch-up
Strangely, Spanish women could stand for parliament but couldn't vote until 1931, and they didn't achieve full suffrage until 1976.

France
Celebrating femme-inism
In 1848, France became one of the first European countries to grant universal male suffrage, but women's rights came much later. They submitted their votes in the first general election since France had been liberated in WWII.

Mexico
A Mexican revolution
The decree recognising the full citizenship of Mexican women was published after decades of fighting for equal rights.

Afghanistan
Voting in Afghanistan
Women gained voting rights after the country won independence in 1919, but this was later overturned and not reinstated until 1964.

Grand Duchy of Finland
A new government with no gender discrimination
Over 100 years ago, Finland's electoral system was radically reformed, with both men and women given unrestricted rights to vote and stand for election. Prior to this the majority of adults didn't qualify for suffrage.

United States
All states are awarded suffrage
There were many women's rights groups in America, and different states granted suffrage at different times. It wasn't until the 19th amendment to the US Constitution that suffrage was declared every citizen's right.

United Kingdom
Political equality
The Equal Franchise Act awarded women and men aged 21 the right to vote. It was the result of many factors, including changing attitudes, suffrage campaigns and the example set by other countries.

Japan
First election where women could vote
Men were awarded suffrage in 1924, but women were not. In fact they didn't receive equal rights until after WWII.

Pakistan
A milestone in Pakistan
It wasn't until 1956 that women were allowed to vote and seats in government were reserved specifically for females.

Switzerland
Still fighting for suffrage in the 70s
A national vote was required to change Switzerland's constitution, and when the government finally held a referendum for women's suffrage, it was rejected by the majority of men. The question wasn't posed again until 1971.

1893 1906 1918 1920 1928 1931 1945 1946 1953 1956 1964 1971

Key figures in the fight for women's rights

Emmeline Pankhurst (1858–1928)
This British suffragette and founder of the Women's Social and Political Union was arrested many times in her fight for women's voting rights.

Kate Sheppard (1847–1934)
After migrating from England to New Zealand, Sheppard campaigned for suffrage through writing to the press and public speaking.

Elizabeth Cady Stanton (1815–1902)
Outraged that women were excluded from an anti-slavery convention, Stanton and fellow abolitionist Lucretia Mott held the first women's rights convention in Seneca Falls, New York.

Hermila Galindo Acosta (1886–1954)
Acosta cocreated the feminist magazine *La Mujer Moderna* and helped to influence changes in divorce law through her political connections.

Sojourner Truth (1797–1883)
When Truth gained her freedom after years of slavery she became a leading abolitionist and champion of women's rights. Her 1851 speech, *Ain't I a Woman?*, challenged attitudes to race and gender.

The Mesoamerican ball game

This violent sport was played to appease the ancient gods and had a gruesome twist at the end

Long before the first football match, the ancient peoples of Mesoamerica were playing their own sport, known as tlachtli, pok-a-tok, ollamaliztli or simply, 'the ball game'.

The Aztec, Mayan and other civilisations all played variants of the game, which had first emerged around 1600 BCE. While the exact rules varied across different cultures and eras, it involved a rubber ball and was played between two competing teams on a stone court. What's also certain is the macabre religious significance it held.

The passing of the ball across the court is thought to have symbolised the movement of the Sun through the sky, moving through night to the next day. Carvings found in the remains of the ball courts depict fertility deities, as well as ritual sacrifices, symbolising the transition from birth, through life and into the afterlife. As well as protective garments, players would also dress in the likeness of animal deities in a bid to draw from their strength and skill during the game.

At the end of each match the winning team would be richly rewarded, while the losing side would be ritually beheaded. Spectators also had much to lose at these games, gambling valuable possessions or even their own children on the outcome. This sport wasn't for the faint-hearted.

Players would strike the rubber ball with their hips, elbows or knees to keep it in play

How to play tlachtli
You could lose more than just your pride in this high-stakes game

1 Pick a court
There were many different sizes and shapes of ball courts, but most were rectangular, built out of stone and enclosed by two sloping or vertical walls. Two carved stone rings were also positioned, one on each wall at the halfway point.

2 Make a ball
The playing ball was made of solid latex rubber harvested from the region's gum trees. These balls weighed approximately four kilograms and could cause serious injury to unprotected body parts.

3 Pick teams
Two teams of two or more players would compete, often including members of the nobility or even tribal leaders. Games were regularly held between rival communities, and captured prisoners were also often compelled to play.

4 Gear up
The only certain rule of tlachtli was that players could not play or strike the ball with their hands, only their shoulders, knees, elbows or hips. Strong animal hides were worn as padding to protect these areas from damage.

5 Game on
The aim of the game was to keep the ball in continuous play, with points scored by landing it in sections of the opponent's half. Successfully hitting the ball through one of the stone rings resulted in instant victory for that team.

6 Make a sacrifice
At the end of the game, the winners would receive rich rewards while the losing team would be beheaded as a sacrifice. This was thought to appease the gods, who were believed to control the movement of the Sun through the sky.

Le Mont Saint-Michel

This medieval monastery is a fortified marvel and one of France's most iconic historic sites

The island of Mont Saint-Michel has survived sieges, fires and revolutions over the centuries. While it was once the destination of thousands of travelling pilgrims, today, the it is a tourist hotspot and a World Heritage site.

Located at the mouth of the river Couesnon, the mount was originally entirely cut off from the mainland at high tide. This provided a natural defence against enemies, as even at low tide the exposed sand flats were treacherous to cross. The Bayeux Tapestry even depicts William the Conqueror's knights falling into the surrounding quicksand. During the 19th century a causeway was built, providing a safer link to the mainland at low tide. In 2014, a permanent two-kilometre-long bridge replaced this, enabling tourists to travel across safely.

The island's fortifications were constructed during the 14th and 15th centuries to defend against English armies during the Hundred Years' War. Cannons abandoned by a besieging English general in 1434 are still on display at the gates. Behind the walls, the village of Mont Saint-Michel stretches around the base of the mount, with winding roads leading to the entrance of the abbey.

Many experts have observed how this layout reflects the hierarchy of medieval society, with the church at the peak of the mount, towering above the shops and houses below. However, after the French Revolution the island was claimed by the new government and converted into a prison. Today, Mont Saint-Michel is still a functioning monastery, and a marvel for visitors.

"Even at low tide the exposed sand flats were treacherous to cross"

The abbey of Mont Saint-Michel was built 80 metres above sea level

The Bayeux Tapestry depicts Mont Saint-Michel and William the Conqueror's knights caught in the surrounding quicksand

5 FACTS ABOUT
MONT SAINT-MICHEL

1 An English twin
Located in Penzance, Cornwall, St Michael's Mount was its English counterpart – the oldest buildings there date back to the 12th century.

2 Tourist boom
Around 2.5 million people visit the island every year, making tourism the town's primary source of income.

3 Tiny population
In 2015 the island was home to just 33 people, including several monks and nuns who live in the abbey quarters.

4 Medieval mount
The site is over 1,300 years old, with the first chapel constructed in 708 CE and dedicated to the Archangel Michael.

5 Tidal power
Mont Saint-Michel Bay experiences some of the highest tides in continental Europe. There can be a difference of up to 15 metres between low and high tide.

Red Star Line

WESTERNLAND

A ferry carrying immigrants docks at Ellis Island, circa 1902-1913

Passengers are inspected by medics on deck upon arrival in 1900

entre Anver
New York Philade

East-Asiatic Company, Limited.
BALTIC AMERICA LINE.

Port of dep
Name of s
Name of N
Date of de
Last resid

Inspecte

UNITE
Seal N
PUBLI

JOURNEY TO AMERICA

During the 19th century millions travelled to seek freedom and fortune in the US

Words by **Tim Williamson**

America, as former President John F Kennedy pointed out, is a nation of immigrants. Today, an overwhelming majority of Americans, from Donald Trump to Kim Kardashian, can find immigrant blood not too far back in their family tree. Some of these ancestors arrived seeking to make their fortune in business or trade, or to find a better quality of life. However, others made the long journey to escape persecution, poverty and even genocide in their land of birth. Towards the end of the 19th century, both these factors led to a huge rise in immigration to the US.

150 years ago there seemed no better prospect than the opportunities and freedoms available in America. After the end of the Civil War in 1865 the country underwent massive restoration, continuing its industrialisation and expansion to the west. Before long it was already surpassing the UK as the world's leading industrial power. The bustling factories and busy dockyards in cities such as New York, Baltimore, Boston and Philadelphia were huge draws for migrants seeking work.

These cities became key destinations for the major transatlantic ferry routes, which in the new age of steam were transporting more people across the ocean, and quicker than ever before. Records for the fastest crossing were smashed almost every year, and rival shipping companies

were in constant competition to build the fastest ships. This meant passengers travelling from Italy, Ireland, Germany, the UK and elsewhere could make the journey across the Atlantic in a few days rather than the previously gruelling ordeal of a few weeks by sail. This fierce competition sometimes resulted in tragedy, such as the sinking of RMS Titanic in 1912.

Catastrophic accidents aside, travelling aboard the liners was a pleasant cruise for first- and second-class passengers, while life for the majority in third class, or steerage, was far less pleasant. These were the cheapest tickets and afforded only cramped living space, with little or no access to the open air on deck. Almost all steerage passengers were migrants from among the poorest of society, and the deck would be filled with accents spanning from the Mediterranean to the Baltic Sea.

Regardless of what they had left behind, for most immigrants the first sight of their new

home was the Statue of Liberty in New York Harbor, at the time a shimmering light brown colour rather than the green we see today. A plaque on the base of the monument reads, "Give us your tired, your poor, your huddled masses yearning to breathe free". It was a welcome to the New World to those travelling from the old.

The largest group to enter the US between 1880–1920 were Italians. Approximately 4 million arrived during this period, a large proportion of whom were men seeking work either in order to settle or to send money back home. In fact, many of those arriving in the US did not look to stay permanently, but hoped to earn a decent wage and then return home. Millions of lira (the old Italian currency) were sent back to the old country by those working in the US, helping to support their families.

At the beginning of the 20th century there were already large Italian-American communities in major US cities, making it easier

Immigration by numbers: 1890–1919

Where did the majority of immigrants come from?

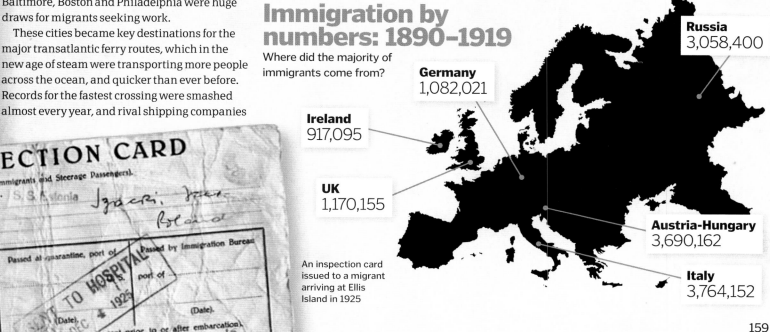

Germany
1,082,021

Ireland
917,095

UK
1,170,155

Russia
3,058,400

Austria-Hungary
3,690,162

Italy
3,764,152

An inspection card issued to a migrant arriving at Ellis Island in 1925

PECTION CARD
(Immigrants and Steerage Passengers).
S. S. Adonia
Passed at quarantine, port of
Passed by Immigration Bureau
SENT TO HOSPITAL
1925
(Date).
No. on ship's list or manifest

for new immigrants to settle. In 1900, New York's Italian population numbered 225,000 – a small but significant minority in a city of 3.4 million. New arrivals would commonly know family members or friends already living within these communities who could assist with finding work and a place to stay.

Other nationalities and groups were not as well established in the US during this period. From the 1880s, Jews living in the Russian Empire faced increased discrimination and were targeted with violence and oppressive laws. Although Jews made up only five per cent of the Russian population at the time, they accounted for 50 per cent of the country's immigrants to the US. Many of them arrived with experience as merchants, tailors and peddlers, bringing with them a range of skills.

America's large cities were already home to large Jewish communities of several nationalities, and the new arrivals from Eastern Europe were able to easily settle in these neighbourhoods, particularly in New York's 'Little Germany' in Lower Manhattan. This nickname was rather misleading, as the area was also home to many Lithuanians, Poles, Ukrainians, Austrians and others. Here, successful second-generation Jewish families were gradually moving out to the expanding suburbs at the city limits, leaving room for others to settle and find their piece of the American Dream.

However, not all Americans were welcoming to what became known as the 'new immigrants', as opposed to first-, second- or even third-generation immigrants from previous decades. In 1892, Ellis Island opened in New York Harbor as the new official facility through which immigrants entering New York would be processed and assessed.

The rules governing those who would and would not be permitted entry became stricter as time went by, with subsequent laws piling on to stop would-be citizens. At first, only those with infectious diseases were sent home or quarantined, then known criminals, then anyone deemed to be 'mentally deficient' or 'feeble-minded'. People were put through often humiliating medical and mental tests to determine whether they were likely to become a burden on society, but relatively few were actually deported as a result.

By the late 1920s, immigration numbers were beginning to fall, before the Great Depression crippled the economy and jobs disappeared. Suddenly it seemed the land of prosperity was no longer the dream many had hoped for. The economic downturn would not last, but immigration numbers would never reach the same highs of previous decades. Nevertheless, the impact and importance of these immigrants-turned-citizens is still apparent today in their descendants.

Immigrants on Ellis Island awaiting inspection

Ellis Island
For over 12 million people, this facility was the gateway to the US

Final steps
Once the final inspection was complete, passengers were free to exchange their money into dollars and buy a train ticket to their next destination, and their new lives.

Registry Room
This large hall was lined with a maze of rails, which formed passengers into orderly lines while they waited for medical and legal inspection.

Detainees
Those who failed medical or legal inspection were held on Ellis Island, either quarantined in hospital or waiting to be sent back home.

Papers, please
Immigration officials checked passengers' documents and asked a series of questions to verify their identity. Any persons judged to be suspicious were detained.

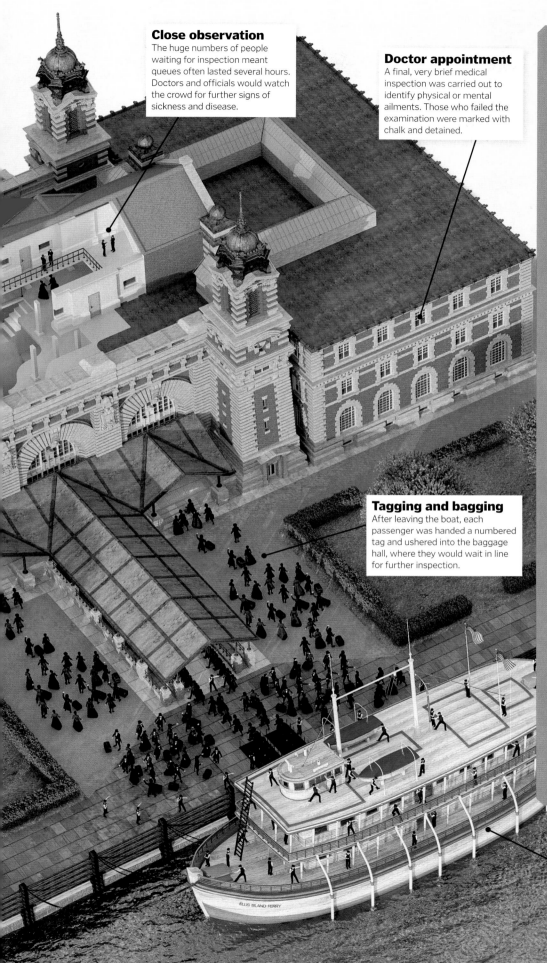

Close observation
The huge numbers of people waiting for inspection meant queues often lasted several hours. Doctors and officials would watch the crowd for further signs of sickness and disease.

Doctor appointment
A final, very brief medical inspection was carried out to identify physical or mental ailments. Those who failed the examination were marked with chalk and detained.

Tagging and bagging
After leaving the boat, each passenger was handed a numbered tag and ushered into the baggage hall, where they would wait in line for further inspection.

On the boat
After arrival in New York Harbor, health inspectors boarded to check for infectious disease among all passengers. Third-class, or 'steerage' ticket holders were then moved for processing on Ellis Island.

The Chinese Exclusion Act

During the 19th century, thousands of Chinese prospectors crossed the Pacific to join the great American Gold Rush that had gripped the world. Later, in the 1860s, thousands more followed to work as labourers, constructing the transcontinental railroad. However, the presence of this Chinese population, although relatively small and centred in San Francisco, California, quickly became a political issue for the entire nation.

In 1882, Congress passed legislation to block all Chinese immigration into the US. This was the first such law that excluded immigration based on nationality or race. Supporters of the Act argued that cheap Chinese labour threatened the American working class – this despite the fact they actually made up a small fraction of the population. Debate surrounding the Act was also laced with racist and xenophobic language. It would not be repealed until 1943, by which time America and China were allies in World War II.

The Chinese Exclusion Act also affected immigrants already living in the US – those who left the country for any reason had to officially apply to reenter

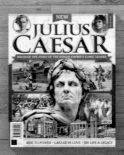